Teacher's Lab Resource
Earth's Surface

interactive SCIENCE

PEARSON

Boston, Massachusetts   Chandler, Arizona   Glenview, Illinois   Upper Saddle River, New Jersey

Safety Reviewers

W. H. Breazeale, Ph.D.
Department of Chemistry
College of Charleston
Charleston, South Carolina

Ruth Hathaway, Ph.D.
Hathaway Consulting
Cape Girardeau, Missouri

Douglas Mandt, M.S.
Science Education Consultant
Edgewood, Washington

Marie A. Ratliff
Science Assessment Specialist
Science Education Consultant
Smithville, Texas

Julie I. Wulff, Ph.D.
Adjunct Professor
National-Louis University
Buffalo Grove, Illinois

ISBN-13: 978-0-13-370547-8
ISBN-10:   0-13-370547-1
2 3 4 5 6 7 8 9 10   V084   13 12 11 10

CONTENTS

CONTENTS (continued)

CONTENTS BY ACTIVITY TYPE

Inquiry Warm-Up

Quick Lab

CONTENTS BY ACTIVITY TYPE (continue

 Quick Lab (continued)

 Lab Investigation

Foundational Research:
Inquiry in the Science Classroom

"How do I know if my students are inquiring?" "If students are busy doing lots of hands-on activities, are they using inquiry?" "What is inquiry, anyway?" If you're confused, you're not alone. Inquiry is the heart and soul of science education, with most of us in continuous pursuit of achieving it with our students.

"Because inquiry is an intellectual pursuit, it cannot merely be characterized by keeping students busy and active."

—Michael J. Padilla
Program Author of *Interactive Science*
Professor of Science Education
University of Georgia
Athens, Georgia

Defining Science Inquiry

What is it? Simply put, inquiry is the intellectual side of science. It is thinking like a scientist—being inquisitive, asking why, and searching for answers. The National Science Education Content Standards define inquiry as the process in which students begin with a question, design an investigation, gather evidence, formulate an answer to the original question, and communicate the investigative process and results. Since it is often difficult to accomplish all this in one class period, the standards also acknowledge that at times students need to practice only one or two inquiry components.

Understanding Inquiry

The National Research Council in Inquiry and the National Science Education Standards (2000) identified several "essential features" of classroom inquiry. We have modified these essential features into questions to guide you in your quest for enhanced and more thoughtful student inquiry.

1. *Who asks the question?* In most curricula, these focusing questions are an element given in the materials. As a teacher, you can look for labs that, at least on a periodic basis, allow students to pursue their own questions.

2. *Who designs the procedures?* To gain experience with the logic underlying experimentation, students need continuous practice with designing procedures. Some labs in which the primary target is content acquisition designate procedures. But others should ask students to do so.

3. *Who decides what data to collect?* Students need practice in determining the data to collect.

4. *Who formulates explanations based upon the data?* Students should be challenged to think—to analyze and draw conclusions based on their data, not just copy answers from the text materials.

5. *Who communicates and justifies the results?* Activities should push students not only to communicate but also to justify their answers. Activities also should be thoughtfully designed and interesting so that students want to share their results and argue about conclusions.

Making Time for Inquiry

One last question—Must each and every activity have students do all of this?

The answer is an obvious and emphatic "No." You will find a great variety of activities in Interactive Science. Some activities focus on content acquisition, and thus they specify the question and most of the procedures. But many others stress in-depth inquiry from start to finish. Because inquiry is an intellectual pursuit, it cannot merely be characterized by keeping students busy and active. Too many students have a knack for being physically but not intellectually engaged in science. It is our job to keep them engaged intellectually.

Evaluator's Checklist

Ask yourself if your science program promotes inquiry by—

✔ Enabling students to pursue their own questions
✔ Allowing students to design their own procedures
✔ Letting students determine what data are best to collect
✔ Challenging students to think critically
✔ Pushing students to justify their answers

MASTER MATERIALS LIST

Interactive Science offers an abundance of activity options to suit your needs. Pearson has worked with Science Kit & Boreal Laboratories to develop Nonconsumable Kits and Consumable Kits that precisely match the needs of the *Interactive Science* labs. Use this Master Materials List or contact your local Pearson sales representative or Science Kit at 1-800-828-7777, or online at http://sciencekit.com. On the following pages, you'll find the materials listed by whether they are nonconsumable or consumable and in which activities the materials are used.

Nonconsumables

Description	Activity Title	Quantity per Class
Apron	Investigating Soils and Drainage (LI)	30
Aquarium	Soil Conservation (QL)	5
Beaker, 250-mL	How Can You Keep Soil From Washing Away? (IW) Using It Up (QL)	10
Beaker, 1000-mL	How Can You Keep Soil From Washing Away? (IW)	5
* Bicycle tires—different	Measuring in Degrees (QL)	10
Board	How Does Gravity Affect Materials on a Slope? (IW)	5
* Books, reference	Dividing History (IW) Modeling the Fossil Record (QL)	
Bowl (dish), small	Erosion Cube (QL) Exploring Geologic Time Through Core Samples (LI) How Fast Can It Fizz? (IW) Sweet Fossils (QL) Weathering and Erosion (QL) Which Layer Is the Oldest? (IW)	5
* Calculator	How Old Is It? (QL)	5
* Coins	Desert Pavement (QL)	
Compass, drafting	Where Are You? (QL)	5
Compass, magnetic	What Is the Land Like Around Your School? (IW)	5
Container, plastic	Investigating Soils and Drainage (LI)	5
Cup, heavy duty plastic	Freezing and Thawing (QL) How Do Glaciers Change the Land? (IW) How Fast Can It Fizz? (IW) It's All on the Surface (QL) Modeling an Asteroid Impact (QL) Rusting Away (QL) The Dating Game (QL)	15
* Digital camera	Reading Satellite Images (QL)	1
Flashlight	Modeling an Asteroid Impact (QL)	5
* Floor	Surging Glaciers (QL)	
* Freezer	Freezing and Thawing (QL) How Do Glaciers Change the Land? (IW)	1
* Globe	2-D and 3-D Maps (QL) How Can You Flatten the Curved Earth? (IW) Where in the World? (QL)	5

KEY:
* = School Supplied
Quantities based on five groups of six students per class.

MASTER MATERIALS LIST (continued)

Nonconsumables

Description	Activity Title	Quantity per Class
Goggles	How Can You Keep Soil From Washing Away? (IW) Investigating Soils and Drainage (LI) Sand Hills (LI)	30
Graduated cylinder, 100-mL	Investigating Soils and Drainage (LI) Weathering and Erosion (QL)	5
* Hallway	Going Back in Time (QL)	1
Hand lens (magnifying)	Exploring Geologic Time Through Core Samples (LI) Freezing and Thawing (QL) The Contents of Soil (QL) Using It Up (QL) What Is Sand Made Of? (IW) What Is Soil? (IW) What's in a Rock? (IW)	5
* Interlocking blocks	Reading Satellite Images (QL)	30
Magnet, circular	How Could Planet Earth Form in Space? (IW)	5
Marble	How Does Gravity Affect Materials on a Slope? (IW)	5
* Mercator projection map	2-D and 3-D Maps (QL)	1
Meter stick	Going Back in Time (QL) Measuring in Degrees (QL) Raindrops Falling (QL) Soil Conservation (QL)	10
Pan, aluminum	A Map in a Pan (LI) Desert Pavement (QL) The Dating Game (QL) Shaping a Coastline (QL)	5
* Pennies	The Dating Game (QL)	500
Petri dish	Raindrops Falling (QL)	5
Plastic sheet, rigid	A Map in a Pan (LI)	10
Protractor	Measuring in Degrees (QL) Weathering and Erosion (QL)	5
Rock, limestone	What's in a Rock? (IW)	5
Rock, sandstone	Freezing and Thawing (QL)	15
Rod, wood	Exploring Geologic Time Through Core Samples (LI)	5
* Rolling pin	Learning From Fossils (QL)	5

x

Nonconsumables

Description	Activity Title	Quantity per Class
Ruler, metric	2-D and 3-D Maps (QL)	5
	A Map in a Pan (LI)	
	Can a Map Show Relief? (IW)	
	Cenozoic Timeline (QL)	
	Desert Pavement (QL)	
	Dividing History (IW)	
	Exploring Geologic Time Through Core Samples (LI)	
	Graphing the Fossil Record (QL)	
	How Can You Keep Soil From Washing Away? (IW)	
	How Did It Form? (QL)	
	How Does Moving Air Affect Sediment? (IW)	
	How Long Till It's Gone? (IW)	
	Learning From Fossils (QL)	
	Make a Pixel Picture (IW)	
	Modeling an Asteroid Impact (QL)	
	Modeling the Fossil Record (QL)	
	Modeling Trace Fossils (QL)	
	Sand Hills (LI)	
	Surface Features (QL)	
	This Is Your Life! (IW)	
	What Is the Land Like Around Your School? (IW)	
Ruler, 15-cm	Shaping a Coastline (QL)	5
* Scissors	Can a Map Show Relief? (IW)	30
	Cenozoic Timeline (QL)	
	Modeling the Fossil Record (QL)	
Spoon, large	How Can You Flatten the Curved Earth? (IW)	5
Spray bottle	Exploring Geologic Time Through Core Samples (LI)	5
Stream table	Modeling Valleys (QL)	1
Timer/stopwatch	How Does Moving Water Wear Away Rocks? (IW)	5
	How Fast Can It Fizz? (IW)	
	Investigating Soils and Drainage (LI)	
	It's All on the Surface (QL)	
	The Dating Game (QL)	
	Weathering and Erosion (QL)	
Tray, plastic	Modeling Landforms (QL)	5
	Sand Hills (LI)	
	Surface Features (QL)	
	The Contents of Soil (QL)	
	Weathering and Erosion (QL)	
	What Is Sand Made Of? (IW)	
Tweezers	The Contents of Soil (QL)	5
Wood block	How Does Gravity Affect Materials on a Slope? (IW)	5

KEY:
* = School Supplied
Quantities based on five groups
of six students per class.

MASTER MATERIALS LIST (continued)

Consumables

Description	Activity Title	Quantity per Class
Antacid tablets	How Fast Can It Fizz? (IW)	10
Bag, zippered	Freezing and Thawing (QL) Modeling an Asteroid Impact (QL) Rusting Away (QL)	15
Ball, polystyrene	Where Are You? (QL)	5
* Barley, bag	Exploring Geologic Time Through Core Samples (LI)	1
* Batteries, D cell	Modeling an Asteroid Impact (QL)	10
* Bottle, 1-L	Soil Conservation (QL)	5
* Bottle, 2-L	Investigating Soils and Drainage (LI)	40
Cardboard, different sizes	Can a Map Show Relief? (IW)	40
Cardboard, white	Modeling an Asteroid Impact (QL)	5
Cheesecloth, pieces	Investigating Soils and Drainage (LI)	20
* Colored pencils	Graphing the Fossil Record (QL) Make a Pixel Picture (IW) Modeling the Fossil Record (QL) What's in a Rock? (IW)	5
* Coffee grounds	Exploring Geologic Time Through Core Samples (LI)	5
* Cornmeal, container	How Does Moving Air Affect Sediment? (IW)	1
Craft sticks	How Can You Keep Soil From Washing Away? (IW) The Contents of Soil (QL) Weathering and Erosion (QL)	30
Cup, plastic	Exploring Geologic Time Through Core Samples (LI)	10
Dropper, plastic	Erosion Cube (QL) Raindrops Falling (QL) Rusting Away (QL)	15
Flour, bag	Desert Pavement (QL) Modeling an Asteroid Impact (QL)	1
* Flowers, split stems	Using It Up (QL)	5
Food coloring, bottle	A Map in a Pan (LI) Using It Up (QL)	1
* Glue	Modeling the Fossil Record (QL)	5
* Graph paper, sheet	2-D and 3-D Maps (QL) Cenozoic Timeline (QL) Graphing the Fossil Record (QL) Make a Pixel Picture (IW) Modeling Landforms (QL) Reading Satellite Images (QL) This Is Your Life! (IW)	30
* Grass and leaves	Exploring Geologic Time Through Core Samples (LI)	

KEY:
* = School Supplied
Quantities based on five groups of six students per class.

Copyright © Pearson Education, Inc., or its affiliates. All rights reserved.

Consumables

Description	Activity Title	Quantity per Class
Gravel/pebbles, bag	How Can You Keep Soil From Washing Away? (IW) Investigating Soils and Drainage (LI)	2
* Ice cubes	Modeling Valleys (QL)	15
Iron filings, container	How Could Planet Earth Form in Space? (IQ)	1
Knives, plastic	How Can You Flatten the Curved Earth? (IW) How Did It Form? (QL) How Long Till It's Gone? (IW) Learning From Fossils (QL) Soil Conservation (QL) Which Layer Is the Oldest? (IW)	30
* Lab report summary	How Old Is It? (QL)	5
* Lentils, bag	Exploring Geologic Time Through Core Samples (LI)	1
Lid, plastic	Surging Glaciers (QL)	5
Marker, felt	How Can You Flatten the Curved Earth? (IW)	5
* Markers	Going Back in Time (QL)	5
Marking pencil, wax	A Map in a Pan (LI) Freezing and Thawing (QL) Investigating Soils and Drainage (LI) It's All on the Surface (QL)	5
* Milk carton	Exploring Geologic Time Through Core Samples (LI)	5
* Millet, bag	Exploring Geologic Time Through Core Samples (LI)	1
Modeling clay, cream	A Map in a Pan (LI) How Can You Keep Soil From Washing Away? (IW) How Did It Form? (QL) How Long Till It's Gone? (IW) Modeling Trace Fossils (QL) Sweet Fossils (QL)	3
Modeling clay, four color	How Did It Form? (QL) Learning From Fossils (QL) Modeling Landforms (QL) Modeling the Fossil Record (QL) Surface Features (QL) Which Layer Is the Oldest? (IW)	10
Modeling clay, orange	How Did It Form? (QL)	4
* Newspaper	Raindrops Falling (QL)	
* Object, small	Modeling Trace Fossils (QL)	5
* Orange or grapefruit	How Can You Flatten the Curved Earth? (IW)	5
Pan, round	How Can You Keep Soil From Washing Away? (IW) How Does Moving Air Affect Sediment? (IW)	10

KEY:
* = School Supplied
Quantities based on five groups
of six students per class.

Consumables

Description	Activity Title	Quantity per Class
Paper clips, box	How Can You Keep Soil From Washing Away? (IW)	1
Paper plates	How Can You Flatten the Curved Earth? (IW) Modeling Trace Fossils (QL) What Is Soil? (IW)	15
* Paper towels	A Map in a Pan (LI) Erosion Cube (QL) How Can You Flatten the Curved Earth? (IW) How Do Glaciers Change the Land? (IW) It's All on the Surface (QL) Surging Glaciers (QL) Sweet Fossils (QL)	20
* Paper, white	A Map in a Pan (LI) Can a Map Show Relief? (IW) Dividing History (IW) Exploring Geologic Time Through Core Samples (LI) Freezing and Thawing (QL) How Can You Keep Soil From Washing Away? (IW) How Could Planet Earth Form in Space? (IW) Modeling the Fossil Record (QL) Sand Hills (LI) What Is Soil? (IW) What Is the Land Like Around Your School? (IW)	30
* Pencil	2-D and 3-D Maps (QL) A Map in a Pan (LI) Can a Map Show Relief? (IW) Measuring in Degrees (QL) Modeling Landforms (QL) Sand Hills (LI) Shaping a Coastline (QL) The Contents of Soil (QL) What Is Soil? (IW) What Is the Land Like Around Your School? (IW) Where Are You? (QL)	5
* Poster board	Going Back In Time (QL)	5
* Rock	Shaping a Coastline (QL) Learning From Fossils (QL)	5
Rubber bands	Investigating Soils and Drainage (LI)	20
Sand, bag	Exploring Geologic Time Through Core Samples (LI) How Do Glaciers Change the Land? (IW) Investigating Soils and Drainage (LI) Sand Hills (LI) Shaping a Coastline (QL) Soil Conservation (QL) What Is Sand Made Of? (IW)	4

KEY:
* = School Supplied
Quantities based on five groups of six students per class.

xiv

Consumables

Description	Activity Title	Quantity per Class
Sand, red	Exploring Geologic Time Through Core Samples (LI)	1
Sandpaper, sheet	How Does Gravity Affect Materials on a Slope? (IW)	3
* Sesame seeds, container	Exploring Geologic Time Through Core Samples (LI)	1
Skewer, barbeque	Sand Hills (LI)	5
Soap, bar	How Do Glaciers Change the Land? (IW) How Does Moving Water Wear Away Rocks? (IW) It's All on the Surface (QL)	10
Soil, bag	Exploring Geologic Time Through Core Samples (LI) How Can You Keep Soil From Washing Away? (IW) Investigating Soils and Drainage (LI) Modeling Valleys (QL) Soil Conservation (QL) Weathering and Erosion (QL)	4
Soil, clay	Investigating Soils and Drainage (LI)	1
Soil, fine texture	Raindrops Falling (QL)	1
Soil sample	The Contents of Soil (QL) What Is Soil? (IW)	1
* Split peas, bag	Exploring Geologic Time Through Core Samples (LI)	1
Spoon, plastic	Exploring Geologic Time Through Core Samples (LI) How Could Planet Earth Form In Space? (IW) How Fast Can It Fizz? (IW) It's All on the Surface (QL) Modeling an Asteroid Impact (QL) Sand Hills (LI) The Contents of Soil (QL) Using It Up (QL) What Is Sand Made Of? (IW)	50
Steel wool, pad	Rusting Away (QL)	10
Straw, flexible	Desert Pavement (QL)	5
Straws, thick	Exploring Geologic Time Through Core Samples (LI)	5
Straws	How Could Planet Earth Form In Space? (IW) How Does Moving Air Affect Sediment? (IW)	10
Sugar cubes	Erosion Cube (QL) Sweet Fossils (QL)	150
* Table, organism groups	Graphing the Fossil Record (QL)	5
* Tape, clear	A Map in a Pan (LI)	1

KEY:
* = School Supplied
Quantities based on five groups
of six students per class.

xv

Consumables

Description	Activity Title	Quantity per Class
Tape, masking roll	2-D and 3-D Maps (QL) Cenozoic Timeline (QL) How Does Gravity Affect Materials on a Slope? (IW) Measuring in Degrees (QL) Sand Hills (LI)	1
Toothpicks, box	The Contents of Soil (QL) What Is Soil? (IW)	1
* Tracing paper	2-D and 3-D Maps (QL) Make a Pixel Picture (IW)	10
Tube, cardboard	Sand Hills (LI)	5
* Water, cold	How Does Moving Water Wear Away Rocks? (IW) It's All on the Surface (QL) Modeling an Asteroid Impact (QL)	
* Water, hot	It's All on the Surface (QL)	
* Water, tap	A Map in a Pan (LI) Erosion Cube (QL) Exploring Geologic Time Through Core Samples (LI) Freezing and Thawing (QL) How Can You Keep Soil From Washing Away? (IW) How Do Glaciers Change the Land? (IW) Investigating Soils and Drainage (LI) It's All on the Surface (QL) Modeling Valleys (QL) Raindrops Falling (QL) Rusting Away (QL) Shaping a Coastline (QL) Soil Conservation (QL) Surging Glaciers (QL) Using It Up (QL) Weathering and Erosion (QL)	
* Water, warm	How Fast Can It Fizz? (IW) Sweet Fossils (QL)	
Wax paper, roll	Learning From Fossils (QL)	1

LABORATORY SAFETY RULES

To prepare yourself to work safely in the laboratory, read the following safety rules. Then read them a second time. Make sure you understand and follow each rule. Ask your teacher to explain any rules you do not understand.

Dress Code

1. To protect yourself from injuring your eyes, wear safety goggles whenever you work with chemicals, glassware, heat sources such as burners, or any substance that might get into your eyes. If you wear contact lenses, notify your teacher.

2. Wear a lab apron or coat whenever you work with corrosive chemicals or substances that can stain.

3. Remove or tie back any article of clothing or jewelry that can hang down and touch chemicals, flames, or equipment. Roll up or secure long sleeves. Never wear open shoes or sandals.

General Precautions

4. Read all directions for an experiment several times before beginning the activity. Carefully follow all written and oral instructions. If you are in doubt about any part of the experiment, ask your teacher for assistance.

5. Never perform activities that are not assigned or authorized by your teacher. Never handle any equipment unless you have specific permission.

6. Never eat or drink in the laboratory.

7. Keep work areas clean and uncluttered. Bring only notebooks, lab manuals, or written lab procedures to the work area. All other items should be left in a designated area.

8. Do not engage in horseplay.

First Aid

9. Report all accidents, injuries, or fires to your teacher, no matter how minor.

10. Learn what to do in cases of specific accidents, such as getting acid in your eyes or on your skin. (Rinse acids from your body with plenty of water.)

11. Be aware of the location of the first-aid kit, but do not use it unless instructed by your teacher. In case of injury, your teacher should administer first aid. Your teacher may also send you to the school nurse or call a physician.

12. Know the location of the emergency equipment such as the fire extinguisher and fire blanket.

13. Know the location of the nearest telephone and whom to contact in an emergency.

Heating and Fire Safety

14. Never use a heat source, such as a candle, burner, or hot plate, without wearing safety goggles.

15. Never heat anything unless instructed to do so. A chemical that is harmless when cool may be dangerous when heated.

16. Never use a flame or spark near a combustible chemical or material.

17. Never reach across a flame.

18. Before using a laboratory burner, make sure you know proper procedures for lighting and adjusting the burner, as demonstrated by your teacher. Do not touch the burner. It may be hot. Never leave a lighted burner unattended. Turn off the burner when it is not in use.

19. Chemicals can splash or boil out of a heated test tube. When heating a substance in a test tube, make sure that the mouth of the tube is not pointed at you or anyone else.

20. Never heat a liquid in a closed container. The expanding gases produced may shatter the container.

21. Before picking up a container that has been heated, first hold the back of your hand near it. If you can feel heat on the back of your hand, the container is too hot to handle. Use an oven mitt to pick up a container that has been heated.

Using Chemicals Safely

22. Never mix chemicals "for the fun of it." You might produce a dangerous, possibly explosive substance.

23. Never put your face near the mouth of a container that holds chemicals. Many chemicals are poisonous. Never touch, taste, or smell a chemical unless you are instructed to do so by your teacher.

24. Use only those chemicals needed in the activity. Read and double-check labels on supply bottles before removing any chemicals. Take only as much as you need. Keep all containers closed when chemicals are not being used.

25. Dispose of excess chemicals as instructed by your teacher. To avoid contamination, never return chemicals to their original containers. Never pour untreated chemicals or other substances into the sink or trash containers.

26. Be extra careful when working with acids or bases. Take extreme care not to spill any material in the laboratory. Wash chemical spills and splashes immediately with plenty of water. Immediately begin rinsing with water any acids that get on your skin or clothing, and notify your teacher of any acid spill.

27. If you are instructed to test for odors, use a wafting motion to direct the odors to your nose. Do not inhale the fumes directly from the container.

28. When mixing an acid and water, always pour the water into the container first and then add the acid to the water. Never pour water into an acid.

Using Glassware Safely

29. Never force glass tubing or thermometers into a rubber stopper or rubber tubing. Have your teacher insert the glass tubing or thermometer if required for an activity.

30. If you are using a laboratory burner, use a wire screen to protect glassware from any flame. Never heat glassware that is not thoroughly dry on the outside.

31. Keep in mind that hot glassware looks cool. Never pick up glassware without first checking to see if it is hot. Use an oven mitt. See rule 21.

32. Never use broken or chipped glassware. If glassware is broken or chipped, notify your teacher and dispose of the glassware in the proper container.

33. Never eat or drink from glassware.

34. Thoroughly clean glassware before putting it away.

Using Sharp Instruments

35. Handle scalpels or other sharp instruments with extreme care. Never cut material toward you; cut away from you.

36. Immediately notify your teacher if you cut your skin when working in the laboratory.

Animal and Plant Safety

37. Never perform experiments that cause pain, discomfort, or harm to animals. This rule applies at home as well as in the classroom.

38. Only handle animals if absolutely necessary. Your teacher will instruct you how to handle each animal species brought into the classroom.

39. If you are allergic to certain plants, molds, or animals, tell your teacher before doing an activity in which these are used.

40. During field work, wear long pants, long sleeves, socks, and closed shoes. Avoid poisonous plants and fungi as well as plants with thorns. Never eat any part of a plant or fungus.

41. Wash your hands thoroughly after any activity involving animals, animal parts, plants, plant parts, or soil.

End-of-Experiment Rules

42. After an experiment has been completed, turn off all burners and unplug all electrical equipment. If you used a gas burner, check that the gas-line valve to the burner is off. Unplug hot plates.

43. Clean up your work area and return all equipment to its proper place.

44. Dispose of waste materials as instructed by you teacher.

45. Wash your hands after every experiment.

SAFETY SYMBOLS

These symbols warn of possible dangers in the laboratory and remind you to work carefully.

 Safety Goggles Wear safety goggles to protect your eyes in any activity involving chemicals, flames or heating, or glassware.

 Lab Apron Wear a laboratory apron to protect your skin and clothing from damage.

 Breakage Handle breakable materials, such as glassware, with care. Do not touch broken glassware.

 Heat-Resistant Gloves Use an oven mitt or other hand protection when handling hot materials, such as hot plates or hot glassware.

 Plastic Gloves Wear disposable plastic gloves when working with harmful chemicals and organisms. Keep your hands away from your face, and dispose of the gloves according to your teacher's instructions.

 Heating Use a clamp or tongs to pick up hot glassware. Do not touch hot objects with your bare hands.

 Flames Before you work with flames, tie back loose hair and clothing. Follow instructions from your teacher about lighting and extinguishing flames.

 No Flames When using flammable materials, make sure there are no flames, sparks, or other exposed heat sources present.

 Corrosive Chemical Avoid getting acid or other corrosive chemicals on your skin or clothing or in your eyes. Do not inhale the vapors. Wash your hands after the activity.

 Poison Do not let any poisonous chemical come into contact with your skin, and do not inhale its vapors. Wash your hands when you are finished with the activity.

Fumes Work in a well-ventilated area when harmful vapors may be involved. Avoid inhaling vapors directly. Only test an odor when directed to do so by your teacher, and use a wafting motion to direct the vapor toward your nose.

 Sharp Object Scissors, scalpels, knives, needles, pins, and tacks can cut your skin. Always direct a sharp edge or point away from yourself and others.

 Animal Safety Treat live or preserved animals or animal parts with care to avoid harming the animals or yourself. Wash your hands when you are finished with the activity.

 Plant Safety Handle plants only as directed by your teacher. If you are allergic to certain plants, tell your teacher; do not do an activity involving those plants. Avoid touching harmful plants such as poison ivy. Wash your hands when you are finished with the activity.

 Electric Shock To avoid electric shock, never use electrical equipment around water, or when the equipment is wet or your hands are wet. Be sure cords are untangled and cannot trip anyone. Unplug equipment not in use.

 Physical Safety When an experiment involves physical activity, avoid injuring yourself or others. Alert your teacher if there is any reason you should not participate.

 Disposal Dispose of chemicals and other laboratory materials safely. Follow the instructions from your teacher.

 Hand Washing Wash your hands thoroughly when finished with an activity. Use soap and warm water. Rinse well.

 General Safety Awareness When this symbol appears, follow the instructions provided. When you are asked to develop your own procedure in a lab, have your teacher approve your plan before you go further.

Name _____ Date _____ Class _____

Laboratory Safety Contract

I, _____,

(please print full name)

have read the Science Safety Rules and Safety Symbols sections, understand
their contents completely, and agree to demonstrate compliance with
all safety rules and guidelines that have been established in each of the
following categories:

(please check)

☐ Dress Code

☐ General Precautions

☐ First Aid

☐ Heating and Fire Safety

☐ Using Chemicals Safely

☐ Using Glassware Safely

☐ Using Sharp Instruments

☐ Animal and Plant Safety

☐ End-of-Experiment Rules

_____
(signature)

Date _____

Student Safety Test: Recognizing Laboratory Safety

Pre-Lab Discussion

An important part of your study of science will be working in a laboratory. In the laboratory, you and your classmates will learn about the natural world by conducting experiments. Working directly with household objects, laboratory equipment, and even living things will help you to better understand the concepts you read about in your textbook or in class.

Most of the laboratory work you will do is quite safe. However, some laboratory equipment, chemicals, and specimens can be dangerous if handled improperly. Laboratory accidents do not just happen. They are caused by carelessness, improper handling of equipment, or inappropriate behavior.

In this investigation, you will learn how to prevent accidents and thus work safely in a laboratory. You will review some safety guidelines and become acquainted with the location and proper use of safety equipment in your classroom laboratory.

Problem

What are the proper practices for working safely in a science laboratory?

Materials (per group)

Science textbook
Laboratory safety equipment (for demonstration)

Procedure

Part 1. Reviewing Laboratory Safety Rules and Symbols

1. Carefully read the list of laboratory safety rules listed on pages xvii and xviii of this lab resource.

2. Special symbols are used throughout this resource to call attention to investigations that require extra caution. Use pages xix and xx as a reference to describe what each symbol means in numbers 1 through 8 in Part 1 under Observations.

Part 2. Location of Safety Equipment in Your Science Laboratory

1. The teacher will point out the location of the safety equipment in your classroom laboratory. Pay special attention to instructions for using such equipment as fire extinguishers, eyewash fountains, fire blankets, safety showers, and items in first-aid kits. Use the space provided in Part 2 under Observations to list the location of all safety equipment in your laboratory.

Name _____ Date _____ Class _____

Recognizing Laboratory Safety (continued)

Observations

Part 1

 1. _____
_____
_____

 2. _____
_____
_____

 3. _____
_____
_____

 4. _____
_____
_____

 5. _____
_____
_____

 6. _____
_____
_____

7. _____
_____
_____

 8. _____
_____
_____

Recognizing Laboratory Safety (continued)

Observations

Part 2

_____

_____

_____

_____

Analyze and Conclude

Look at each of the following drawings and explain why the laboratory activities pictured are unsafe.

1. _____

_____

_____

_____

2. _____

_____

_____

_____

3. _____

_____

_____

_____

Recognizing Laboratory Safety (continued)

Critical Thinking and Applications

In each of the following situations, write *yes* if the proper safety procedures are being followed and *no* if they are not. Then give a reason for your answer.

1. Gina is thirsty. She rinses a beaker with water, refills it with water, and takes a drink.

   _____

   _____

2. Bram noticed that the electrical cord on his microscope is frayed near the plug. He takes the microscope to his teacher and asks for permission to use another one.

   _____

   _____

3. The printed directions in the lab book tell a student to pour a small amount of hydrochloric acid into a beaker. Jamal puts on safety goggles before pouring the acid into the beaker.

   _____

   _____

4. It is rather warm in the laboratory during a late spring day. Anna slips off her shoes and walks barefoot to the sink to clean her glassware.

   _____

   _____

5. While washing glassware, Mike splashes some water on Evon. To get even, Evon splashes him back.

   _____

   _____

6. During an experiment, Lindsey decides to mix two chemicals that the lab procedure does not say to mix, because she is curious about what will happen.

   _____

   _____

Laboratory Skills Checkup 1

Following Directions

1. Read all of the following directions before you do anything.

2. Print your name, last name first, then your first name and middle initial (if you have one), at the top of this page.

3. Draw a line through the word "all" in direction 1.

4. Underline the word "directions" in direction 1.

5. In direction 2, circle the words "your first name."

6. In direction 3, place an "X" in front of the word "through."

7. Cross out the numbers of the even-numbered directions above.

8. In direction 7, cross out the word "above" and write the word "below" above it.

9. Write "Following directions is easy" under your name at the top of this page.

10. In direction 9, add the following sentence after the word "page": "That's what you think!"

11. Draw a square in the upper right corner of this page.

12. Draw a triangle in the lower left corner of this page.

13. Place a circle in the center of the square.

14. Place an "X" in the center of the triangle.

15. Now that you have read all the directions as instructed in direction 1, follow directions 2 and 16 only.

16. Please do not give away what this test is about by saying anything or doing anything to alert your classmates. If you have reached this direction, make believe you are still writing. See how many of your classmates really know how to follow directions.

Laboratory Skills Checkup 2

Defining Elements of Scientific Inquiry

Laboratory activities and experiments involve the process of scientific inquiry. Listed in the left column are the names of parts of this method. The right column contains definitions. Next to each word in the left column, write the letter of the definition that best matches that word.

_____ 1. Hypothesis

    A. Prediction about the outcome of an experiment

_____ 2. Manipulated Variable

    B. What you measure or observe to obtain your results

_____ 3. Responding Variable

    C. Measurements and other observations

_____ 4. Controlling Variables

    D. Statement that sums up what you learn from an experiment

_____ 5. Observation

    E. Factor that is changed in an experiment

_____ 6. Data

    F. What the person performing the activity sees, hears, feels, smells, or tastes

_____ 7. Conclusion

    G. Keeping all variables the same except the manipulated variable

Laboratory Skills Checkup 3

Analyzing Elements of Scientific Inquiry

Read the following statements and then answer the questions.

1. You and your friend are walking along a beach in Maine on January 15, at 8:00 A.M.

2. You notice a thermometer on a nearby building that reads –1°C.

3. You also notice that there is snow on the roof of the building and icicles hanging from the roof.

4. You further notice a pool of seawater in the sand near the ocean.

5. Your friend looks at the icicles and the pool and says, "Why is the water on the roof frozen and the seawater is not?"

6. You answer, "I think that the salt in the seawater keeps it from freezing at –1°C."

7. You go on to say, "And I think under the same conditions, the same thing will happen tomorrow."

8. Your friend asks, "How can you be sure?" You answer, "I'm going to get some fresh water and some salt water and expose them to a temperature of –1°C and see what happens."

Questions

A. In which statement is a **prediction** made? _____

B. Which statement identifies a **problem**? _____

C. In which statement is an **experiment** described? _____

D. Which statement contains a **hypothesis**? _____

E. Which statements contain **data**? _____

F. Which statements describe **observations**? _____

Laboratory Skills Checkup 4

Performing an Experiment

Read the following statements and then answer the questions.

1. A scientist wants to find out why seawater freezes at a lower temperature than fresh water.

2. The scientist goes to the library and reads a number of articles about the physical properties of solutions.

3. The scientist also reads about the composition of seawater.

4. The scientist travels to a nearby beach and observes the conditions there. The scientist notes the taste of the seawater and other factors such as waves, wind, air pressure, temperature, and humidity.

5. After considering all this information, the scientist sits at a desk and writes, "If seawater has salt in it, it will freeze at a lower temperature than fresh water."

6. The scientist goes back to the laboratory and does the following:
   a. Fills each of two beakers with 1 liter of fresh water.
   b. Dissolves 35 grams of table salt in one of the beakers.
   c. Places both beakers in a freezer at a temperature of –1°C.
   d. Leaves the beakers in the freezer for 24 hours.

7. After 24 hours, the scientist examines both beakers and finds the fresh water to be frozen. The salt water is still liquid.

8. The scientist writes in a notebook, "It appears that salt water freezes at a lower temperature than fresh water does."

9. The scientist continues, "I suggest that the reason seawater freezes at a lower temperature is that seawater contains dissolved salts, while fresh water does not."

Questions

A. Which statement(s) contain **conclusions**? _____

B. Which statement(s) contain a **hypothesis**? _____

C. Which statement(s) contain **observations**? _____

D. Which statement(s) describe an **experiment**? _____

E. In which statement is the **problem** described? _____

F. Which statement(s) contain **data**? _____

G. What is the **manipulated variable** in the experiment? _____

H. What is the **responding variable** in the experiment? _____

Laboratory Skills Checkup 5

Identifying Errors

Read the following paragraph and then answer the questions.

Andrew arrived at school and went directly to his Earth science class. He took off his cap and coat and sat down at his desk. His teacher gave him a large rock and asked him to find its density. Realizing that the rock was too large to work with, Andrew got a hammer from the supply cabinet and hit the rock several times until he broke off a chip small enough to work with. He partly filled a graduated cylinder with water and suspended the rock in the water. The water level rose 2 cm. Andrew committed this measurement to memory. He next weighed the rock on a balance. The rock weighed 4 oz. Andrew then calculated the density of the rock as follows: He divided 2 cm by 4 oz. He then reported to his teacher that the density of the rock was .5 cm/oz.

Questions

1. What safety rule(s) did Andrew break? _____
   _____

2. What mistake did Andrew make using measurement units?
   _____
   _____

3. What should Andrew have done with his data rather than commit them to memory?
   _____
   _____

4. What is wrong with the statement, "He next weighed the rock on a balance"?
   _____
   _____

5. Why is "4 oz" an inappropriate measurement in a science experiment?
   _____
   _____

6. What mistake did Andrew make in calculating density?
   _____
   _____

Mapping Earth's Surface

Exploring Earth's Surface

? Answering the Big Question

The activities in this lesson will help students answer the Big Question by having them define *topography* and examine how topography is represented on a map.

What Is the Land Like Around Your School?

Inquiry Focus

Form an Operational Definition—using words to create a working definition of the term *topography*

Group Size   Individuals or pairs

Class Time   10 minutes

Procedure Tips

1. If a compass is unavailable, point out north to students.
2. If necessary, give students an idea of how far away a kilometer is by referring to a local landmark that is approximately one kilometer from your school.

Answers

1. Sample Answer: mostly flat with hilly areas to the south and west
2. The model is a two-dimensional representation of a three-dimensional area on Earth.
3. Sample Answer: Topography describes the features of an area, especially elevation.

Surface Features

Unlocking the Key Concept

This activity will help students understand the difference between elevation and relief.

Inquiry Focus

Measure—using a ruler to determine the elevation of features on a land's surface

Group Size   Groups

Class Time   20 minutes

Answers

1. Sample Answer: 20 cm—this measurement should be the largest of all the measurements; 5 cm—this measurement should be smaller than the mountain
2. Sample Answer: 20 cm − 5 cm = 15 cm (relief)
3. Sample Answer: I would take the path that has the lowest elevation and lowest relief, as that would be easiest to cross.

Modeling Landforms

⚷ Unlocking the Key Concept

This activity will help students visualize the differences and similarities among the three major types of landforms.

Inquiry Focus

Make Models—creating physical representations of the three major landforms

Group Size   Individuals or pairs

Class Time   20 minutes

Advance Preparation   (10 minutes)

Obtain the clay and provide each student or pair of students with a large lemon-sized ball of each color.

Procedure Tips

So that you can reuse the clay, tell students not to mix the colors when connecting the landforms.

Answers

1. Sample Answer: They are similar because both are models of the three major types of landforms. They are different because the drawings are two-dimensional and the clay models are three-dimensional.
2. Sample Table:

Landform	Elevation	Relief
Plain	Low	Low
Plateau	High	Low
Mountain	High	High

Models of Earth

Answering the Big Question

The activities in this lesson will help students answer the Big Question by having them make and use maps and globes, examine map projections, measure distances in degrees, and locate points on maps using knowledge of latitude and longitude.

Inquiry Warm-Up

How Can You Flatten the Curved Earth?

Inquiry Focus

Observe—using the senses to gather information to make and interpret a fruit-peel map

Group Size Pairs or groups

Class Time 15 minutes

Safety

Remind students to be careful when using the knife to score the fruit's peel.

Advance Preparation (15 minutes)

1. If appropriate, ask each student or pair of students to bring a large orange or grapefruit from home.
2. Have several globes available that can be shared by students.
3. Make sure the felt-tip pens are able to produce thin but dark lines on the fruit peel.
4. Fruit can be expensive. Larger groups can be assigned if only a few pieces of fruit are available for each class.

Procedure Tips

1. Point out that the continents need only be roughly sketched onto the peel.
2. Instruct students to use the knife to score the peel through an ocean so as to lessen the damage to a continent outline.
3. Encourage students to be patient while peeling the fruit.
4. Have the students wash their hands before handling the fruit.

Answers

1. The peel cannot be placed completely flush against the table or desktop. To do so would require stretching or tearing the peel.

2. The only way to show the continents on a flat map is to distort some portion of Earth's surface. Some students might know that most maps distort different parts of Earth's surface in some way.

Quick Lab

2-D and 3-D Maps

Unlocking the Key Concept

This activity will help students observe how a map projection and a globe can both be used to represent Earth and how a map projection, because it is a 2-D image, can distort shapes, sizes, and distances of our 3-D planet.

Inquiry Focus

Observe—using the senses to compare and contrast land near the equators and poles on both a map projection and a globe

Group Size Pairs

Class Time 20 minutes

Advance Preparation (15 minutes)

Provide each student with a black and white copy of a Mercator projection with the same scale as the globes that will be used for this lab. If possible, obtain enough globes so that students can work in pairs. Alternatively, have pairs share available globes.

Alternative Materials

Wax paper and a permanent, fine-line grease pencil can be substituted for the tracing paper and sharp pencil. However, tell students to handle the wax paper carefully to avoid wrinkling it.

Procedure Tips

1. Tell students to use only enough tape to affix the corners of the papers to the desktop. Four small pieces should be sufficient.
2. Stress that the land traced in a set of squares must be exactly the same area to ensure that accurate comparisons can be made.
3. Make sure students lay the tracing paper (or wax paper) completely flat against the globe when tracing.

Answers

1. On Mercator projections, the sizes and shapes of the land areas near the equator are less distorted than land areas closer to the poles. On a globe, the land areas are accurate in size and shape anywhere.

2. Look for answers that include reasoning such as: because a globe is a sphere, like Earth, distances, shapes, and sizes are accurate everywhere on the globe.

Quick Lab

Measuring in Degrees

🔑 **Unlocking the Key Concept**

This activity will introduce students to the concept of how distances are measured on Earth by having them measure distances on a circle in degrees.

Inquiry Focus

Measure—collecting quantitative data using a protractor to measure degrees around a circle

Group Size Pairs

Class Time 15 minutes

Advanced Preparation (10 minutes)

1. On each lab bench or desk, place two pieces of masking tape 50 cm apart.

2. Place 12 pieces of masking tape at 30-degree intervals around the entire tire or hoop. Label the pieces from Point A through Point L.

Alternative Materials

Plastic hoops, the rims of buckets, or similar items can be substituted for the bicycle tires.

Procedure Tips

Show students how the meter sticks can be used to help extrapolate lines on the protractor to the edge of the circle.

Answers

1. 360°
2. 30°
3. Look for answers that include the fact that because Earth's surface is curved, measuring in degrees is much easier and more accurate than trying to measure straight lines.

Quick Lab

Where in the World?

🔑 **Unlocking the Key Concept**

This activity will help students become familiar with locating places on Earth using lines of latitude and longitude.

Inquiry Focus

Observe—using the senses to locate cities at given latitudes and longitudes

Group Size Individuals or pairs

Class Time 10 minutes

Advance Preparation (10 minutes)

If possible, obtain enough globes so that students can work alone or in pairs. Make sure each globe shows all six cities in the table.

Procedure Tips

As an extra question, have students determine what word the first letter of each city spells out (*globes*).

Sample Data

Latitude	Longitude	City and Country
2°S	79°W	Guayaquil, Ecuador
38°N	9°W	Lisbon, Portugal
34°N	135°E	Osaka, Japan
34°S	58°W	Buenos Aires, Argentina
55°N	3°W	Edinburgh, Great Britain
1°N	103°E	Singapore, Singapore

Answers

1. Singapore
2. Edinburgh
3. Sample Answer: New York City, New York 40°N 73°W; Melbourne, Australia 37°S 144°E; Cairo, Egypt 30°N 31°E

Mapping Technology

Answering the Big Question

The activities in this lesson will help students answer the Big Question by having them investigate how technology, such as satellites and GPS, can be used in mapmaking.

Make a Pixel Picture

Inquiry Focus

Analyze Models and Systems—evaluating how accurately a pixel image represents objects

Group Size Pairs

Class Time 15 minutes

Procedure Tips

Make sure the graph paper squares are visible through the tracing paper.

Answers

1. Sample Answer: No; the pixel picture does not have the same shape.
2. Sample Answer: Use smaller squares in the grid, and the pixel picture will look more like the apple.
3. Look for answers that explain that the monitor should have more pixels, which would allow images to appear in more detail.

Reading Satellite Images

Unlocking the Key Concept

This activity will help students better understand how data collected from above Earth's surface is used to create different types of maps of the planet.

Inquiry Focus

Make Models—using information from aerial photographs to make maps

Group Size Pairs

Class Time 20 minutes

Safety

Instruct students to take extra caution when using the digital cameras, especially if the cameras are not their own. You might instruct them to loop the carrying strap around their wrists to prevent dropping the cameras.

Advance Preparation (20 minutes)

1. If time is short, provide photographs of the model neighborhood.
2. Draw your own map of the model and use it as an example for students who have trouble understanding the concept.
3. Place the model on a lab table where it can be easily accessed.
4. You will need a computer, a printer, and photo paper in order to print students' pictures.

Alternative Materials

Clay or wooden blocks can also be used to make the neighborhood model.

Procedure Tips

1. Suggest that the students take pictures of different sections of the model so they can capture more detail. Also suggest that they make sure the photos include some overlap.
2. Remove the model after the students have taken their pictures.
3. You might wish to explain how the scale of their maps can be determined and how a scale drawing of the model can be made.

Answers

1. Sample Answer: houses, roads, and trees
2. Sample Answer: City planners might use aerial photography to get a better idea of where to place new buildings.
3. Look for answers that suggest that the photographs allow you to see the locations of all the features you would want to put on a map.
4. The photo shows exactly what the neighborhood looks like, but the map is easier to use to find your way around.

Where Are You?

Unlocking the Key Concept

This activity will help students understand how GPS works.

Inquiry Focus

Make Models—creating a model of a GPS satellite system

Group Size Pairs

Class Time 15 minutes

Safety

Caution students to take care while using the drafting compasses.

Procedure Tips

1. Students may have trouble using the compass on the foam ball. Suggest that one student hold the ball while the other one carefully draws the circle.
2. Sample Answer for Procedure Step 4: 2.

Answers

1. Each circle represents the distance from anywhere on the circle to my point.
2. It represents the area of an object being tracked by GPS satellites.
3. Only a general area would be identified, which would include the area where the two circles intersect; 3 satellites.

Topographic Maps

❓ Answering the Big Question

The activities in this lesson will help students answer the Big Question by having them make and use topographic maps to understand concepts such as relief and two-dimensional representations.

Inquiry Warm-Up

Can a Map Show Relief?

Inquiry Focus

Make Models—creating a physical representation of the relief of a cardboard landscape

Group Size Individuals

Class Time 15 minutes

Safety

Remind students to be careful when using scissors and to report any cuts to you immediately.

Advance Preparation (25 minutes)

Cut the cardboard pieces in advance. Suggested sizes of the pieces, in centimeters, are 4 × 4, 6 × 8, 8 × 10, 10 × 12, 12 × 14, 16 × 18, 18 × 22, and 20 × 26. Thicker cardstock works best for this activity.

Procedure Tips

It might be useful for students to tape the sheets of paper to their work areas so the papers don't shift as they trace the cardboard pieces.

Answers

1. Both are models of the same landscape. The stack of cardboard is a three-dimensional model, whereas the tracing is a two-dimensional model.
2. The lines on the paper represent contour lines, which are lines that show points of equal elevation in an area.
3. The architect needs the location of any trees or boulders that would be expensive to remove, any significant slopes (hills, gullies, holes), or any areas that may flood.

Lab Investigation

A Map in a Pan

🔑 Unlocking the Key Concept

Both Versions This activity will help students simulate the process of making a topographic map by making a three-dimensional model and representing it on a two-dimensional map.

Answers—Pre Lab
Both Versions:

1. Students will be constructing two types of models: a landform (the hill) and a map.
2. Students will be interpreting a topographic map.

Inquiry Focus
Both Versions:

Make Models—creating a physical representation of a hypothetical hill
Interpret Data—analyzing and drawing conclusions from a simple topographic map

Group Size

Directed Inquiry Individuals or pairs
Open Inquiry Pairs

Class Time

Directed Inquiry 40 minutes
Open Inquiry 55 minutes

Materials
Both Versions:

An aluminum baking pan or plastic shoebox is a good choice for the deep-sided pan. A plastic shoe storage box is sturdier than an aluminum pan and is preferred because it can be used many times. Be sure that the pan is smaller than the sheets.

Safety
Both Versions:

Have rags or paper towels available to wipe up any spills.

Advance Preparation (1 hour)
Both Versions:

1. Gather enough pans for each student or group.
2. Cut a rectangular piece of clear plastic for each student or group. This plastic is available at building or hardware stores and most craft supply stores; it could be cut to order or cut from large sheets with a utility knife.
3. To save additional time, you might wish to color the water ahead of time and distribute the colored water to students.

Alternative Materials
Directed Inquiry:

If clear, hard plastic is unavailable, individual overhead transparency sheets can be used.

Open Inquiry:

Erasable markers work well on the transparency sheet and can be cleaned quickly for the next class to use the same materials.

Procedure Tips
Both Versions:

1. Encourage students to tape a clear transparency sheet on top of the clear, hard sheet of plastic to make their map. When they are finished with their contours, it is easier to remove the transparency sheet and sandwich it between two pieces of unlined white paper to trace their map.
2. Suggest that students select two reference points to use to put the plastic or transparency sheet back down in exactly the same place each time after adding water.
3. In order to save time during the lab, you may want to have students build the model the day before and allow it to dry overnight.

4. Encourage the students to use the metric ruler to create a vertical 1-cm scale on the side of the pan so that the water depth is more accurate for mapping elevation on their models.

Open Inquiry:

1. Sample Prediction for Procedure Step 3: Accept all reasonable predictions. For example, if students made a model hill, the map of the hill would have many contour lines close together to show that the hill was steep.
2. Sample Answer to Procedure Step 4a: It is a line connecting locations of equal elevation on a topographic map.
3. Sample Answer to Procedure Step 4b: The difference in elevation from one contour line to the next. Sample Answers: 10 feet, 20 feet, 5 meters
4. Sample Answer to Procedure Step 4c: Yes.
5. Sample Answer to Procedure Step 4d: Yes. A possible extension is to have the students use the topographic symbols provided in the text to create both natural (swamp, forests, rivers) and cultural features (buildings, airports, roads) on their maps.
6. Sample Answer to Procedure Step 4e: By pouring water into the container in equal elevation increments. Emphasize scale.

Answers—Analyze and Conclude
Directed Inquiry:

1. Both are models of a landform (hill). The clay hill is a three-dimensional model whereas the topographic map is a two-dimensional model of the hill.
2. Closely-spaced contour lines represent steep slopes; widely-spaced contour lines represent gentle slopes.
3. The highest point on the map is represented by the innermost circular contour line.
4. Ridges and valleys are represented by V-shaped contour lines. V-shaped contour lines that point downhill indicate a ridge. V-shaped contour lines that point uphill indicate a valley.
5. Sample Answer: The map could be improved by adding a map key, which includes the contour interval, or by decreasing the contour interval to make the map more detailed.

MAPPING EARTH'S SURFACE

Open Inquiry:

1. Look for answers that indicate that a model is used to represent something that cannot be seen or measured directly.

2. Look for answers that clearly state the ways the map was like and different from the landform. The answer could take the form of a table or a Venn diagram. Encourage the students to list how they could improve their procedure.

3. The model would change elevation quickly. The hill would be steeply sloped.

4. Contour lines are very close together in an area of high relief and farther apart in an area of low relief. The contour interval is very low in areas of high relief (steep slope); conversely, the contour interval is very high in areas of low relief (no slope).

Answers—Post Lab

Directed Inquiry:

1. The water would not have made contact with the edges of the hill and therefore wouldn't have provided a contour line.

2. Because the crater is a depression, it would be shown by circular contour lines marked with small dashes to indicate a depression.

3. Look for answers that include at least one specific statement about what the student learned, such as how to make a topographic map or how to interpret it. Answers about what students still want to know should relate to topographic map-making processes or interpretation of such maps.

Communicate—Look for answers that include a clear comparison. For example, one map might have more closely spaced contour lines, because the model had a steep hill.

Open Inquiry:

1. Sample Answer: We found that our procedures were not informative enough to make a detailed contour map. We would change the way in which we marked areas of equal elevation.

2. Sample Answer: Hikers use topographic maps in order to assess the difficulty of the trails they will be hiking. People building a house might want to consider the topography of the region in which they will be building. Someone wishing to establish a farm or industrial complex in a particular area might be concerned about the topography of that area.

3. Sample Answer: I've learned that topographic maps can show the shapes and sizes of landscape features. Topographic maps also show the land's relief using contour lines. I would like to know more about how natural disasters change topographical features in an area.

Communicate—Lead a class discussion about which process was easier—model to map or map to model—and why. Have photocopies of several simple topographic maps and a photograph of the landforms that were mapped so the students can compare them to their model.

What Is the Land Like Around Your School?

Forces at Earth's surface as well as those deep inside the planet constantly change the shape of the land. In this activity, you will describe the land around your school and determine what type of model you have made of the area.

INQUIRY FOCUS Form an Operational Definition

Procedure

Materials

piece of plain paper
pencil
magnetic compass
metric ruler

1. In the middle of a piece of plain paper, draw a small square (about 3 cm × 3 cm) to represent your school.

2. Choose a word that describes the type of land near your school, such as *flat*, *hilly*, *sloping*, or *mountainous*. Write the word inside the square.

3. Use a magnetic compass to determine the direction of north. On your paper, assume that north is at the top of the page. Mark north with a capital *N*.

4. If you travel due north 1 km from your school, what type of land would you see? Again, choose a word to describe the land in this area. Write that word to the north of the square.

5. Repeat Step 4 for areas located 1 km east, south, and west of your school.

Think It Over

1 What phrase could you use to describe the land areas around your school?

_____

2 What type of model is your drawing? Be specific.

_____

_____

3 Based on your observations, how could you define *topography*?

_____

_____

Quick Lab

20 min

Surface Features

Topography refers to the shape of the land in an area. In this activity, you will learn how to measure the elevation and relief of landforms, and to understand the difference between the two terms.

INQUIRY FOCUS Measure

Procedure

Materials

modeling clay
plastic tray
metric ruler

1. With your group, use the clay to make a model of three landforms in one area: a mountain, a hilly area, and a flat area. Build the model in the plastic tray. For this model, you will treat the bottom of the plastic tray as sea level.

2. Use the ruler to measure the height of the mountain from sea level. Record this measurement. _____ cm

3. Now measure the highest point on the flat area from sea level. Record this measurement. _____ cm

4. Study the hilly area. Find the lowest point and highest point as measured from sea level. Record these measurements.

   Highest point: _____ cm

   Lowest point: _____ cm

Think It Over

1. What is the elevation of the mountain? The flat land?

_____

2. The relief of an area is the difference in elevation between the highest and lowest points. Calculate the relief of the hilly area.

_____

3. In terms of elevation and relief, what path would you take from one side of your land to the other side? Explain.

_____

_____

Name _____ Date _____ Class _____

Modeling Landforms

All landforms have different combinations of elevation and relief. In this activity, you will draw side views and construct models of the three major landforms: plains, mountains, and plateaus.

INQUIRY FOCUS Make Models

Procedure

1. Use your pencil to divide the graph paper along its longer edge into three equal parts. Label each part with the name of one major landform.

2. On the paper, draw a profile, or side, view of each major landform in the correct space.

3. On the board or tray, make a three-dimensional model of each major landform. Use a different color of clay for each model.

4. Carefully move the clay landforms to form an unbroken landscape.

Materials

piece of graph paper
pencil
board or cafeteria tray
three colors of
    modeling clay

Think It Over

① How are your drawings and clay models the same? How do they differ?

_____

_____

_____

② In the space below, make a table to compare and contrast the elevation and relief of the three major types of landforms. Use the terms *high* and *low* in your table.

11

EXPLORING EARTH'S SURFACE

Name _____ Date _____ Class _____

How Can You Flatten the Curved Earth?

Most maps are two-dimensional models of a three dimensional object. In this activity, you will observe what happens when you try to make a simple map of Earth's continents.

INQUIRY FOCUS Observe

Procedure

Materials

globe
felt-tip permanent pen
large orange or grapefruit
plastic serrated knife
large metal spoon
paper towels
paper plates

1. Use the globe to observe the positions of Earth's continents relative to one another.

2. Using the felt-tip pen, make a rough sketch of the outlines of the continents on the surface of the fruit. Let the marker dry for a minute or two.

3. ✂ Using the plastic knife, carefully make a *shallow* cut in the peel from the top to the bottom of the fruit. Take care not to cut into the fruit itself.

4. Slowly and carefully insert the spoon under one side of the cut and wiggle it around under the peel. Continue wiggling and moving the spoon until you can't move it any farther (the handle of the spoon will get in the way).

5. Pull out the spoon and slide it into the other side of the cut. Repeat Steps 3 and 4 until the peel is free of the orange itself. Try to keep the peel in one or two large pieces so that the continents remain intact. If this is not possible, try to produce as few pieces of peel as possible. Place the peeled fruit on the paper plate. Wipe up any juice with a paper towel.

6. 🖐 Try to lay the peel flat on a table or your desktop and observe the map you just made. Wash your hands.

Think It Over

1 What happened to the peel when you tried to flatten it on the table?

_____

2 Is there any way to keep the shapes of the continents from being distorted when trying to represent them on a flat surface? Explain.

_____

Quick Lab ●————————● **20 min**

2-D and 3-D Maps

Maps and globes show shapes, sizes, and positions of Earth's surface features. Map projections are used to show Earth's curved surface on a flat map. In this activity, you will compare and contrast a map projection and a globe.

INQUIRY FOCUS Observe

Procedure

Materials

graph paper
tracing paper
masking tape
metric ruler
Mercator projection map
globe
sharp pencil

1. Tape the graph paper to your desktop. Place the tracing paper on top of the graph paper. Line up the edges of the papers. Tape the tracing paper to the desktop.

2. Use the graph paper and ruler as guides to draw four squares on the tracing paper. Each square should be 4 cm × 4 cm. Draw two of the squares side by side at the top of the page. Draw the other two squares side by side along the bottom edges of the page. Label the top two squares "Equator" and the bottom two squares "Poles."

3. Carefully remove the tracing paper from the desktop. Place one of the top squares over an area of land near the equator on the Mercator projection. Carefully trace the outline of the land. Position the other top square over the same area of land on the globe and trace the outline of the land. Label each square as either "Mercator projection" or "Globe."

4. Repeat Step 3 using the bottom two squares and an area of land close to one of Earth's poles. Label each square.

Think It Over

1 Compare the sizes and shapes of the land areas in both sets of squares.

_____

_____

_____

2 On which model of Earth—the map projection or the globe—are distances, shapes, and sizes most accurate? Why?

_____

_____

15 min

Measuring in Degrees

Degrees are used to measure the distance around a circle. Degrees can also be used to measure distances on the surface of a sphere, such as Earth. In this activity, you will measure distances around a circle in degrees.

INQUIRY FOCUS Measure

Procedure

Materials

pencil
protractor
masking tape
two meter sticks
bicycle tires of
   different sizes

1. Using a meter stick, measure the distance between the outside edges of two pieces of tape on the table. Record your measurement. _____ cm

2. Try to measure the distance along the tire between two pieces of tape using the meter stick. What makes it difficult?

   _____

3. Lay a bicycle tire flat on your table. Place one meter stick from the center of the tire to Point A. Place a second meter stick from the center of the tire to Point B.

4. Using the protractor, measure the angle between the two meter sticks. Record your measurement. _____ cm

5. Using the protractor, measure the angle between each consecutive set of points on the tire. (For example, B and C, then C and D, etc.) Record your measurements.

   _____

Think It Over

1 What is the distance, in degrees, around a circle?

   _____

2 How far, in degrees, is Point A from Point B?

   _____

3 Why do we measure distances on Earth's surface in degrees?

   _____

Name _____ Date_____ Class_____

_____

Where in the World?

Lines of latitude and longitude form a grid that can be used to find locations anywhere on Earth. In this activity, you will use latitude and longitude coordinates to locate six cities around the world.

INQUIRY FOCUS Observe

Procedure

1. Observe the globe. Locate the equator and the prime meridian.

2. Use the globe to determine the city located at or closest to each of the locations listed in the table. Write the name of each city and its country in the correct space.

Materials

globe

Latitude	Longitude	City and Country
2°S	79°W	
38°N	9°W	
34°N	135°E	
34°S	58°W	
55°N	3°W	
1°N	103°E	

Think It Over

1 Which city is closest to the equator?

_____

2 Which city is closest to the prime meridian?

_____

3 Choose three major cities not listed in the table and determine the latitude and longitude of each.

_____

_____

_____

MODELS OF EARTH

Make a Pixel Picture

A picture element, or pixel, is the smallest bit of information in an image. Pixels are usually arranged in a grid and are often dots or squares. In this activity, you will construct a grid and use it to make a pixel picture.

INQUIRY FOCUS Analyze Models and Systems

Procedure

1. Use a black pencil to draw the outline of an apple on the graph paper. Your apple should be about 10 cm in diameter.

2. Place the tracing paper on top of the graph paper. Use a red pencil to fill in each centimeter square of the graph paper that is completely inside the outline of the apple. If a square is mostly inside the apple, fill it in too. If a square is mostly or completely outside the apple's outline, leave it blank. *Note: Each square must be either entirely red or entirely blank.*

3. Each square on the grid represents a pixel of the image. How many pixels make up the apple in your image?

_____

Materials

metric ruler
metric graph paper
tracing paper
black pencil
red colored pencil

Think It Over

1 Pick up the tracing paper and look at the image. Can you recognize an apple? Explain.

_____

_____

2 Can you think of a way to change this activity to get a more accurate picture of the apple?

_____

_____

3 If you were shopping for a computer monitor, would you select one with more pixels or fewer pixels? Why?

_____

_____

Name _____ Date _____ Class _____

20 min

Reading Satellite Images

Most maps today are made using data collected from aerial photographs and satellites. In this activity, you will answer questions about how these technologies are used to make maps.

INQUIRY FOCUS Make Models

Procedure

Materials

digital camera
interlocking plastic
  toy bricks or blocks
metric graph paper

1. Your teacher will provide the class with a three-dimensional model of a neighborhood made of interlocking plastic toy bricks.

2. ⚠ Using the digital camera, take a series of photographs of the neighborhood model from directly overhead. *Note: Hold the digital camera securely when using it.*

3. Make prints of the digital images. Using the prints, draw a map of the neighborhood to an appropriate scale on the graph paper.

4. Write a key explaining the scale of your map and include it on the map.

Think It Over

1 What types of features are you able to see in the photographs?

_____

_____

2 How might aerial photography be used by city planners?

_____

_____

3 Why are the photographs helpful when making a map?

_____

_____

4 Your photo and your map are both models of the neighborhood. How are the photo and the map similar? How are they different?

_____

_____

Quick Lab ● 15 min

Where Are You?

GPS is an important tool used by modern mapmakers. In this activity, you will learn how a GPS system works by using a model of one to find a specific location.

INQUIRY FOCUS Make Models

Procedure

Materials
round polystyrene
  foam ball
drafting compass
pencil

1. On the foam ball, draw a circle that goes completely around the widest part of the ball. This represents Earth's equator.

2. Choose three places on the ball and mark them with dots. Label these three dots Points A, B, and C. In your model, a GPS satellite is positioned above each of these three points.

3. ✂ Locate the two points that are farthest apart. Set the compass to a distance greater than halfway between these two points.

4. Using the compass, draw a circle with Point A at the center. Then draw the same size circle with Point B at the center. At how many points do these two circles meet?

_____

5. Draw a third circle the same size with Point C at the center. Shade in the area where these three circles intersect.

Think It Over

1 What do the three circles represent?

_____

_____

2 What does the shaded area represent?

_____

_____

3 How accurately would two satellites of a GPS system pinpoint your location? How many satellites would be needed to determine an exact location?

_____

_____

_____

Can a Map Show Relief?

Relief is the difference in elevation between the highest and lowest parts of an area. On a topographic map, elevation and relief are shown with contour lines. In this activity, you will make a relief map of a landscape.

INQUIRY FOCUS Make Models

Procedure

1. ✂ Use the scissors to carefully cut off the corners of each of the eight pieces of cardboard so that they appear rounded. Each piece should be at least 1 cm smaller in each direction than the next larger piece.

2. Trim the long sides of the two largest pieces so that the long sides appear wavy. Don't cut more than 0.5 cm off the cardboard.

3. Trace the outline of the largest cardboard piece onto the sheet of paper.

4. Trace the next largest piece of cardboard inside the tracing of the first cardboard piece. Don't let any lines cross.

5. Trace the other cardboard pieces, from largest to smallest, one inside the other, on the same paper.

6. Stack the cardboard pieces next to the paper in the same order they were traced.

Materials

8 pieces of cardboard of descending sizes
scissors
sheet of unlined paper
pencil
metric ruler

Think It Over

1 Compare the stack of cardboard pieces with your drawing. How are they alike? How are they different?

_____

_____

_____

2 If the cardboard pieces model a landform, what do the lines on the paper represent?

_____

3 An architect is planning where to build a house on a piece of land. What other features would the architect need in a topographical map besides elevation?

_____

PRE LAB

A Map in a Pan

Reviewing Content

A topographic map is a model that shows the surface features of an area. A topographic map uses contour lines to show how elevation, relief, and slope change in an area. A contour line connects points with the same elevation. A group of contour lines stacked in a circle indicates a hill. The innermost contour line in the group marks the top of the hill. V-shaped contour lines that point downhill indicate a ridge. V-shaped contour lines that point uphill indicate a valley. Contour lines that are close together indicate a steep slope while contour lines that are farther apart represent a gentle slope. Contour lines never intersect or end.

Reviewing Inquiry Focus

Scientists make models to represent objects or processes. This is because the objects might be too small or too large to be observed directly. It is also because some processes occur too fast or too slow to be observed directly. Maps are models that show all or part of Earth as seen from above. Maps are interpreted so you can learn more about Earth and its features.

1 In this investigation, what types of models will you be constructing?

_____

_____

2 What type of map will you be interpreting in this investigation?

_____

DIRECTED Inquiry ●————————————● 40 min

A Map in a Pan
Problem

How can you make a topographic map?

INQUIRY FOCUS
Make Models,
Interpret Data

Materials

deep-sided pan
pitcher of water
food coloring
pencil
marking pencil
modeling clay
clear, hard sheet
   of plastic
metric ruler
sheet of unlined
   paper
clear tape
paper towels

Procedure

1. [icon] Place a lump of the modeling clay on the bottom of the pan. Shape the clay into a model of a hill. The hill should be no higher than the top of the pan.

2. Use a pencil to stir 5 drops of food coloring into the water. The water should be just dark enough to show up clearly against the clay hill.

3. Hold the ruler vertically against the inside of the pan. Pour the colored water into the pan to a depth of 1 cm. This represents sea level.

4. Place the sheet of hard, clear plastic over the top of the container. Trace the outline of the pan on the plastic sheet with the marking pencil.

5. With the plastic sheet in its correct place, look straight down into the pan and trace the outline the water makes around the edges of the clay model. Make sure the plastic sheet does not move as you make your tracing. Remove the plastic sheet from the pan.

6. Add another centimeter of water to the pan, bringing the depth of the water to 2 cm. Replace the plastic sheet exactly as before, then trace the water level again.

7. Repeat Steps 5 and 6 several times. Stop when the next addition of water would completely cover your model.

8. Remove the plastic sheet and place it under your sheet of unlined paper. Trace the outlines that you drew on the plastic sheet onto the sheet of paper.

9. Trim the edges of your paper and tape it in the space on the next page.

TOPOGRAPHIC MAPS

Analyze and Conclude

1 **Make Models** Compare your map with the clay landform. How are they alike? How are they different?

_____

_____

_____

_____

2 **Interpret Data** Look at your map. How can you tell from the map which parts of your model hill have a steep slope? A gentle slope?

_____

_____

_____

_____

3 **Observe** How can you tell from the map which point on the hill is highest?

_____

_____

_____

4 **Draw Conclusions** Suppose there was a ridge along one side of your hill and that a valley separated the ridge and the hill. How could you show the ridge and the hill on your topographic map?

_____

_____

_____

5 **Infer** How could you improve your topographic map?

_____

_____

_____

_____

POST LAB

A Map in a Pan

1 **Infer** Why did you not completely cover your model hill with water?

_____

_____

_____

2 **Interpret Data** Suppose your hill was a volcano with a large crater at the top. How would you show the crater on your map?

_____

_____

_____

3 **Summarize** Describe what you learned in this lab about making a topographic map of a model landform and what questions you still have.

What I learned

_____

_____

_____

What I still want to know

_____

_____

_____

_____

Communicate

Compare your map to at least three others. Identify at least two things that are the same for all the maps. Also describe differences among the maps.

OPEN Inquiry ●━━━━━━━━━ 55 min

A Map in a Pan
Problem

INQUIRY FOCUS
Make Models.
Draw Conclusions

How can you make a topographic map?

Materials

deep-sided pan

water, 1 L

marker or marking
  pencil

modeling clay

clear, hard sheet of
  plastic

2 clear transparency
  sheets

tape

metric ruler

sheet of unlined
  white paper

pencil

food coloring
  (optional)

Design an Experiment

1. Topographic maps show the elevation of Earth's natural surface features, such as mountains, hills, valleys, and lakes, as well as the cultural features of a small part of Earth's surface. You will be provided with a set of materials to be used to create your own topographic map. You and your lab partner will create a landform and a way to map the landform. You will then trade your map with another group for interpretation.

2. 🖐 🦺 With your lab partner, shape the modeling clay into a landform you would like to map. You can consult your student edition for possible landform features to construct. Your model can assume any shape, given the limits of the amount of clay and the size and height of the pan. Your model must be able to fit easily inside of the pan and cannot be higher than the sides of the pan.

3. 🧼 Wash your hands with warm water and soap when you are finished with your model.

4. Predict what you think the topographic map of your model will look like. Draw your prediction of the map in the space provided.

TOPOGRAPHIC MAPS

A MAP IN A PAN *continued*

OPEN Inquiry

Lab Investigation

5. Consider the following questions as you design a procedure for making a topographic map of your model:

    a. What is a contour line?

    b. What is a contour interval? What will your contour interval be?

    c. Should the contour intervals that you draw remain consistent throughout all parts of the map?

    d. Will you be using any topographic symbols in the activity other than contour lines?

    e. How will you consistently map the elevations on your model?

6. ⚠ Write out your step-by-step procedure for creating your topographic map. Have your teacher approve your plan, then carry out your procedure and create your topographic map.

Procedure

_____

_____

_____

_____

_____

_____

_____

_____

_____

_____

TOPOGRAPHIC MAPS

OPEN Inquiry

Lab Investigation

Analyze and Conclude

1 **Make Models** Why do scientists build models?

_____

_____

_____

_____

2 **Draw Conclusions** Compare your map with the clay landform. How are they alike? How are they different? How could you improve your map as a model of the landform?

_____

_____

_____

_____

_____

3 **Predict** What do you think a model of a hill might look like if its map had contour lines that were very close together?

_____

_____

4 **Infer** How do contour lines differ in an area of high relief versus an area of low relief? How does the contour interval change?

_____

_____

_____

_____

TOPOGRAPHIC MAPS

Name _____ Date_____ Class_____

POST LAB

A Map in a Pan

1 Design an Experiment Scientists follow a method of experimentation and learn from their results. As you began creating the topographic map of your model by following your procedures, did you observe some steps that could have been better written? What changes would you have made?

_____

_____

_____

2 Infer With your partner, create a list of situations from everyday life in which a topographic map would be useful. Explain why a topographic map would be the best map for use in the given situation.

_____

_____

_____

3 Summarize Describe what you learned in this lab about making a model of Earth's surface. What do you still want to know?

What I learned _____

_____

_____

What I still want to know _____

_____

_____

_____

Communicate

Join forces with another lab group. Your task is to "reverse" the investigation process by obtaining a topographic map from your teacher and using clay to build a model hill to represent a portion of the map. Your group should explain in detail the process you used to create your landform. Share the explanation of how you changed your procedure based on doing the reverse process. Upon completion, compare your model to the actual landform.

Weathering and Soil

Rocks and Weathering

❓ Answering the Big Question

The activities in this lesson will help students answer the Big Question by allowing them to explore how mechanical and chemical weathering occurs, and to test variables that determine how fast it occurs.

Inquiry Warm-Up

How Fast Can It Fizz?

Inquiry Focus

Draw Conclusions—collecting data to test a hypothesis about the dissolving rate of antacid tablets, and relating that to weathering

Group Size Individuals or pairs

Class Time 10 minutes

Safety

Students should wear goggles to avoid getting splashed in the eye by fizzing antacid.

Advance Preparation (20 minutes)

Grind up tablets using the spoon and a plastic bowl. Leave the powder in the bowl for each lab group.

Procedure Tips

1. Supply each student or pair with one whole tablet and one ground-up tablet.
2. Have students use warm water from the tap.
3. If stopwatches are unavailable, students can observe a second hand on a watch or clock.
4. Sample Hypothesis for Procedure Step 2: Smaller particles of antacid will dissolve faster than larger particles.

Answers

1. The ground-up tablet should dissolve faster. Typical dissolving times are 30 seconds for the whole tablet, and 10 seconds for the ground-up tablet. Answers will vary depending on each student's original hypothesis.
2. The variable was whether the tablet was whole or broken into pieces. This means dissolving time was based on the surface area of the tablet.
3. Some students might conclude that rocks broken into smaller pieces will weather faster.

Quick Lab

Freezing and Thawing

🔑 Unlocking the Key Concept

This activity will help students demonstrate the way ice can break down rocks and how it is a major force of mechanical weathering.

Inquiry Focus

Observe—recording changes in the appearance of rocks to determine whether or not mechanical weathering has occurred

Group Size Pairs

Class Time 10 minutes, plus 5 minutes on the second day and 10 minutes on the third day

Safety

Students should wear goggles to avoid getting possible rock grains in their eyes.

Advance Preparation (15 minutes)

1. Gather several samples of sandstone. Choose samples whose grains are fairly well cemented and won't rub off easily when handled. Each pair of students should be supplied with three rocks of similar size.
2. To shorten the class time needed to complete the activity, consider doing the lab's initial step—soaking the rocks overnight—in advance.

Procedure Tips

1. Remind students that water expands when it freezes and turns into ice. Tell students to keep this in mind as they make observations during the investigation.
2. Explain to students that some of the material holding the grains together might also dissolve during the soaking. This could also explain the presence of some of the grains in the plastic bags. Explain that if this is the case, then chemical weathering has also occurred.
3. Try experimenting with different rock types, both those that are granular and those that are fractured. You might need to repeat the procedure several times. Compare these results with the students' results.

Answers

1. Students should observe that grains of rock have broken off of the rock sample that was soaked in water before freezing. They might even note that they can rub the rock's surface and remove even more grains.

2. Look for answers that include the fact that water expands as it freezes. This would cause any ice that formed in the pore spaces to act as a wedge pushing the individual grains apart.

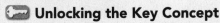

Quick Lab

Rusting Away

🔑 Unlocking the Key Concept

This activity will help students demonstrate a major form of chemical weathering, and show how it aids mechanical weathering in breaking down rock.

Inquiry Focus

Predict—observing and recording data to test a prediction about the effect of water and oxygen on steel wool

Group Size Pairs

Class Time 5 minutes, then 5 minutes three days later

Safety

Safety goggles and gloves should be worn while students are examining the rusty steel wool. Small particles could become airborne or stuck to fingers and clothing. Some steel wool might feel sharp. Caution students to take care while handling both pieces.

Advance Preparation (10 minutes)

1. Cut steel wool pads into pieces about 4 cm × 4 cm.

2. Do not use the steel wool pads that contain soap.

Procedure Tips

1. When students moisten the pads, ensure that they only dampen them.

2. Sample Prediction for Procedure Step 2: The steel wool in the bag will get rusty.

Answers

1. Look for answers that describe the pad breaking down and a confirmation or correction of the students' predictions.

2. The new pad springs back and keeps its shape when squeezed. The pad that was left in the bag crumbles and stays compacted when squeezed. It is beginning to turn rust colored.

3. Oxidation, a type of chemical weathering, can break down the surface of rocks that contain iron, making them soft and crumbly. This would make it easier for mechanical weathering to break the rock into smaller pieces.

Quick Lab

It's All on the Surface

🔑 Unlocking the Key Concept

This activity will help students understand the different rates of weathering by showing how different conditions can affect how fast weathering occurs.

Inquiry Focus

Infer—observing and interpreting results to analyze the effect of water temperature on dissolving rates

Group Size Pairs

Class Time 20 minutes

Safety

Caution students to be careful when filling their cups with hot water. Tell students to use the hot mitt when handling the cup containing hot water.

Advance Preparation (15 minutes)

1. To save time and prevent mess, cut the bars of soap into equal pieces of about 2 cm × 3 cm before class.

2. Fill several pitchers with ice water and room temperature water just before class begins.

Alternative Materials

Watches or a clock can be substituted for the stopwatches.

Procedure Tips

1. Plain bar soap with no extra additives provides the best results.

2. Cafeteria trays can be used so all three cups can be carried to the lab station at the same time.

3. Encourage students to look at the soap throughout the 5-minute intervals and note what they see.

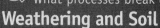
4. Sample Hypothesis for Procedure Step 1:
Weathering takes place faster in warmer
conditions than in colder conditions.

Answers
1. The soap in the cup with the hot tap water
dissolved the fastest.
2. Warmer conditions allow for faster dissolving.
3. Sample Answer: Water temperature affects the
rate at which the soap dissolves and could also
affect the rate of chemical weathering in rock.
Chemical weathering in warmer climates
occurs faster than in colder climates.

How Soil Forms

Answering the Big Question

The activities in this lesson will help students
answer the Big Question by having them examine soil to discover its components, explore the
permeability of soil, and identify organic and
inorganic substances within soil.

What Is Soil?

Inquiry Focus
Form an Operational Definition—using observation to formulate a definition of soil

Group Size Individuals

Class Time 15 minutes

Safety
1. Safety goggles should be worn while students
are handling and studying the soil.
2. Students should wash their hands after handling the soil.

Advance Preparation (10 minutes)
Prepare a sample of 50 mL of soil on a paper
plate for each student.

Procedure Tips
1. Before students begin the activity, review
the types of materials they might see in soil:
pieces of rock and minerals, pieces of plants
(such as leaves, roots, or seeds), and insect
parts. You might choose to use several different types of samples so that students can see
that all soils are not the same.

2. Charts that show visual percentages of light
and dark grains might be useful for estimat-
ing the percent composition in Question 2.

Answers
1. Operational definitions should include the
concept that soil is composed of different
types of particles, including sand, clay, rock,
mineral fragments, and material derived
from living things.
2. Sample Answer: Black dirt—60%; Sand
grains—25%; Rock and mineral pieces—7%;
Plant parts—5%; Insect parts—3%. Some
students might also know that soil contains
air and water.

Investigating Soils and Drainage

Unlocking the Key Concept
Both Versions This activity will help students
understand the differences in soils by having
them create physical representations of various types of soils to determine how fast water
drains through them.

Answers—Pre Lab
Both Versions:
1. This is a model of water (possibly precipita-
tion) draining through different types of soil.
2. Quantitative data, because a process will be
timed with a watch to determine a certain
number of seconds or minutes.

Inquiry Focus
Make Models—using various materials and soil
components to make a variety of soils in order
to test their permeability
Observe—using the senses to gather information about the porosity and permeability of
various kinds of soil

Open Inquiry:
Observe—using the senses to gather information about the porosity and permeability of
various kinds of soil
Measure—collecting quantitative data about how
fast water drains through various kinds of soil
Design an Experiment—using controlled conditions to test the rate of water flow through different kinds of soil

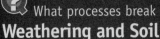
Group Size

Both Versions Groups

Class Time

Both Versions 35 minutes

Safety

Both Versions:

1. Students should wear safety goggles when working with soil and sand.
2. Aprons should be worn to avoid getting wet.

Alternative Materials

Both Versions:

Large plastic or metal funnels can be used instead of the upper bottle. Coffee filters can be used instead of the gauze or cheesecloth.

Advance Preparation (25 minutes)

Both Versions:

1. To save time and ensure safety, cut the bottles for students before the lab. Figure out how many group setups you will need. Each group will need eight plastic 2-L bottles for its setup. Cut the tops off four of the bottles for each setup. Cut the bottoms off four additional bottles for each setup. Punch a hole in the bottles with tops removed, above the water level and below the place where the two bottles will meet. Refer to the diagram of the setup in the Directed Inquiry as you prepare the bottles.
2. To save time, prepare soil samples before the class period. To ensure uniform dryness of the soils, heat the samples at a low temperature on a pan in an oven or let them dry in an area with low humidity before the lab.

Procedure Tips

Both Versions:

1. Students should fill the upper bottle about halfway with soil and pat it lightly.
2. Students should plan to pour a lot more than the marked volume of water through the setup because the soil will absorb and retain some water. Students should pour the same quantity of water for each soil sample.

Directed Inquiry:

Sample Prediction for Procedure Step 6: Water will drain most quickly through soils with the largest particles, because the pore spaces between the particles are big and allow water to pass most freely. Water will drain most slowly through soils that have tiny particles and pore spaces, which retain water.

Open Inquiry:

1. Demonstrate porosity and permeability to students, as follows:

   a. Place a large jar, beaker, or fish bowl on a demonstration table. Have containers of the following hidden beneath the demo table: ping pong balls, gravel, sand, and a large beaker of water. Ask, **Is the container full?** *(The container is empty.)* Point out that, in truth, the container is full of air at the moment.

   b. Pour in the ping pong balls close to the top of the container. Ask, **Is the container full?** *(Lead the students to state that the ping pong balls have displaced the air. Some will say that the container is now full.)*

   c. Pour in the gravel. It will displace some of the ping pong balls and fill in some empty spaces. Pour in as much gravel as possible. You can even jiggle the container a bit. Ask, **Is the container full?** *(Many will say yes, but some will start to get the idea and start thinking about your demo and say no.)*

   d. Pour in the sand. It will fill in the spaces between the gravel and ping pong balls; the container will hold quite a bit of sand. Ask, **Is the container full?** *(It appears to now be full.)*

   e. Pour in the beaker of water. As you pour the water in, it is interesting to have the students note the measurement of how much water can still be poured into the "full" container. When the container can hold no more water, Ask, **Is the container full?** *(yes)*

2. Sample Answer to Procedure Step 3a: Porosity is how much water a material can hold. Soil is porous.

3. Sample Answer to Procedure Step 3b: Permeability is how easily a gas or a liquid can move through a material. Sandstone.

4. Sample Prediction for Procedure Step 5: If water is poured through soils with varying pore sizes, then the water will flow fastest through the soil with the largest pore size.

Answers—Analyze and Conclude

Directed Inquiry:

1. The water drained fastest through the sand. It drained the slowest through the clay mixed with soil.

2. The water moves into the pore spaces in the soil, moving down through connecting spaces until it drains out of the bottom of the layer of soil.

3. The rate is dependent on the size of pore spaces in the soil and how well connected they are.

4. No. The amounts would vary depending on how much water each soil sample retained.

5. The bed should be sand because it will allow water to drain away from plant roots better.

Open Inquiry:

1. Look for answers that come from the students' data tables showing which materials allowed the most water to flow through the fastest.

2. Look for answers that come from the data collected through experimentation. Look for answers that correlate particle size with water flow through the materials.

3. The porosity of the material varies, thus affecting the permeability.

4. The water would flow quickly through the soil to the bedrock. The roots of the plants would not have enough time to absorb the water. Farmers would have to use expensive irrigation or grow plants that require quick drainage.

5. Look for answers involving the impermeability of asphalt over a large flat area that has no constructed drainage.

Answers—Post Lab

Directed Inquiry:

1. Look for answers that include an understanding of why their results agreed or disagreed with their predictions.

2. Sample Answer: Collect soils from different areas rather than make up our own mixtures. Accept any change that students can support as an improvement in the procedure or one that will allow better data collection.

3. Look for answers that reflect the students' comprehension of the fact that larger soil particles have larger pore spaces, allowing water to move through more easily. Accept reasonable answers regarding what they still want to know.

Communicate—Student tips might include adding the water at a constant rate for all samples, refilling the graduated cylinder quickly, and patting the soil samples with identical pressure.

Open Inquiry:

1. Sample Answer: Incorrect measurement, inaccurate timing, not following the procedures exactly for each experiment, and not keeping the amount of soil or water constant are all possible sources of error.

2. Look for answers that restate the hypothesis and use the gathered data to support the group's decision to accept or reject the hypothesis.

3. Answers should reflect the students' comprehension of the fact that larger soil particles have larger pore spaces, allowing water to move through more easily. Accept reasonable answers regarding what they still want to know.

Communicate—See the grading rubric on the next page.

Quick Lab

The Contents of Soil

🔑 Unlocking the Key Concept

This activity will help students examine soil to discover the substances, both organic and inorganic, that are within it.

Inquiry Focus

Classify—placing substances present in soil into recognized categories based on their observable characteristics

Group Size Pairs

Class Time 15 minutes

Safety

1. Have students wear safety goggles throughout this activity.

2. Students should wash their hands with warm water and soap after handling soil samples.

Advance Preparation (25 minutes)

1. Prepare a soil sample for each pair of students before class. If possible, use soil from your local area. The soil should be dry so that separation and sorting are easy.

2. Set up a place where the students can return their samples.

Alternative Materials

If you are unable to collect the soil outdoors in your area, potting soil can be used.

Procedure Tips

1. Remind students that soil contains both organic and inorganic materials. Review the definition of each category of materials with students.

   • Organic Material: Organic material in soil is alive or was once alive. This material can be plant particles, such as roots, leaves or seeds; insect parts, such as wings or body parts; or it can even be feces left behind by scavenging mice. Decayed plant or animal material in soil is called humus.

   • Inorganic Material: Inorganic material is the part of soil that is not and never was living. It consists mostly of weathered rock and minerals. These particles will be fairly small but should resemble the rocks or minerals from which they were weathered.

   • Tell students that the third category in their table can contain organic or inorganic material. They should place materials in this category if they cannot definitely identify them as either organic or inorganic substances.

2. Have students use the hand lens to look for rock particles, insects, pieces of plant matter, and other organic or inorganic materials.

3. Sample Answer to Procedure Step 3: See the sample data table on the next page.

Answers

1. Sample Answer: Organic: dead leaves; Inorganic: pieces of rock; Unknown: fragment of dark, spongy material

2. Sample Answer: Plant parts drop onto the soil surface and decay; Decayed plant material is mixed into the top layer of the soil; Insects that have burrowed into soil die and decay.

Soil Conservation

❓ Answering the Big Question

The activities in this lesson will help students answer the Big Question by allowing them to explore various ways erosion can damage soil and the methods that can be used to conserve soil.

Inquiry Warm-Up

How Can You Keep Soil From Washing Away?

Inquiry Focus

Observe—using senses to gather information on the best way to keep soil from washing down a slope

Group Size Pairs

Class Time 15 minutes

Safety

1. Safety goggles should be worn while students are handling the soil.

2. Students should wash their hands once they are finished with the lab.

Grading Rubric—Open Inquiry

	Grading Rubric				
	4 —Well organized, clearly stated, detailed presentation.	3—Organized but not clearly stated. Details were not given.	2 – Disorganized with no details. Data were not mentioned.	1—Unable to present complete experimental findings.	0—Not able to present.
a					
b					
c					
d					
e					
f					

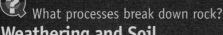
Advance Preparation (10 minutes)

To save time and avoid potential mess, fill the large beakers with soil before class.

Procedure Tips

Encourage students to be creative in their arrangements.

Answers

1. Students' answers should indicate an understanding of the need to impede the downslope movement of soil and water. Students might also choose to describe the best arrangement.

2. Look for answers that include methods that protected the surface of the soil or were able to bind particles of soil together, such as covering the surface of the soil with strips of paper.

Quick Lab

Using It Up

🔑 Unlocking the Key Concept

This activity will help students examine the way plants take up nutrients from the soil.

Inquiry Focus

Predict—using prior knowledge and experience to describe what will happen to the flower in the water

Group Size Pairs

Class Time 15 minutes, plus 10 minutes the next day

Safety

Students should wear aprons to prevent possible staining of their clothes by the food coloring.

Advance Preparation (30 minutes)

1. Prepare the split flowers for students in advance. Carnations work well. After purchasing the flowers, keep them in water.

2. To prepare the flowers, split each stem in half lengthwise with a sharp knife or razor blade. The split should reach halfway up the stem. To stop the stem from continuing to split, place a piece of masking tape around the upper end of the cut.

3. Take the flowers out of the water a couple of hours before class.

4. Trim the ends of the stems just before class to make them as fresh as possible. Trimming the stems on an angle will make it easier to lift or prop the stem off the bottom of the beaker, thus allowing better uptake of the water.

Alternative Materials

As a substitute for carnations, use celery stalks that have leaves.

Procedure Tips

1. Have students do this lab in an out-of-the-way place in your classroom.

2. After setting up the flower in the two beakers, students will have to lean the top of the flower against an object for support.

3. When students examine the results, remind them to look only at the portions of the stems that are above the water level, as the stem portion that is in the water becomes stained on the outside from the food coloring itself.

4. Sample Prediction for Procedure Step 3: The part of the flower on the colored water side will become colored.

Sample Data Table—The Contents of Soil

Contents of Soil		
Organic	**Inorganic**	**Unknown**
1. Pieces of plant root	1. Pieces of weathered bedrock	1. Fragments of unidentified material of unknown origin
2. Shreds of dried leaves, grass, or other plant materials	2. Pieces of trash	
3. Insects or insect parts.	3. Metal or glass fragments	

Answers

1. Students should observe a change of color in the stem and flower petals on the side of the flower with its stem in the colored water. Look for answers that explain why their observations are or are not in agreement with their predictions.

2. The plant absorbed the food color "nutrients" with the water. Plants growing in soil take in water and nutrients through their roots, and these spread throughout the plants through their stems.

3. Over time, plants can remove so many of the nutrients from the soil that the soil loses its fertility.

Quick Lab

Soil Conservation

🗝 Unlocking the Key Concept

This activity will help students explore the ways that soil can be conserved.

Inquiry Focus

Predict—using prior knowledge and experience to predict what will happen to the soil on a model hillside when exposed to flowing water

Group Size Groups

Class Time 20 minutes

Safety

1. Have students wear safety goggles during the investigation.

2. Students should wash hands thoroughly after handling soil.

Advance Preparation (25 minutes)

1. Prepare the soil/sand mixture for students before class. Students should use a slightly damp soil/sand mixture to make their hills. Make sure it is not soggy.

2. Prepare the top of the soda bottle cap as follows: Hold a needle with pliers. Heat the needle in a flame. Use the hot needle to melt small holes in the plastic cap. Each group will need one bottle and cap.

Alternative Materials

A rimmed baking sheet, a shallow plastic tub or a similar container can be used instead of an aquarium.

Procedure Tips

1. Before students begin, review the two methods of soil conservation used in the investigation.
   - *Contour plowing* is plowing fields across a slope instead of up and down the slope.
   - *Terracing* is the creation of a series of level areas on a steep hillside.

Note that some students will plow their hills straight up and down the slope. This is *not* a soil conservation measure, but should allow students to compare lack of soil conservation with contour plowing and terracing.

2. Split the class into three groups. Assign the students in each group a different method of preparing the soil.

3. Look for models that show students have taken the shape of the hill and how it would affect runoff into account.

4. The volume of water sprinkled on the soil should model moderate rainfall. Too much water and students will end up with a pool of mud; not enough water and students won't observe erosion.

5. Tell students to continue sprinkling until they observe results on their hillside.

6. Sample Prediction for Procedure Step 3: Plowing up and down the hill will cause the most erosion. Terracing and contour plowing slow erosion by breaking the flow of water running down the slope.

Answers

1. Answers will depend on students' predictions. Both contour plowing and terracing should limit erosion. Students who "plow" furrows straight up and down their hill should see the most soil erosion because this is not a method of soil conservation.

2. Plowing across a slope, as in contour plowing, minimizes the amount of soil washing downhill. Terracing a hillside creates level areas that hold water and soil and prevents them from washing down steep slopes. Plowing down the slope of a hill does not conserve soil, because it allows water to freely run downhill, carrying soil with it.

Inquiry Warm-Up ● 10 min

How Fast Can It Fizz?

Weathering is the process that causes rocks to break down at Earth's surface. In this activity, you will use antacid tablets to explore one factor that affects the time it takes weathering to occur.

INQUIRY FOCUS Draw Conclusions

Procedure

1. 🥽 Put on your goggles.

2. In this activity, the whole antacid tablet represents solid rock. The ground-up tablet represents pieces of rock. Write a hypothesis that explains how the two tablets will dissolve in water.

   _____

3. Have one person hold the stopwatch and be prepared to start it the moment water touches the tablet.

4. Place the whole antacid tablet in one of the cups. Then pour in 100 mL of warm water. Stir with the spoon until the tablet is completely dissolved. Use the stopwatch to time how long it takes. Record the time.

   _____

5. Place the ground-up tablet in the second cup. Repeat Steps 3 and 4.

   _____

Materials

2 antacid tablets (one whole, one ground up)
2 plastic cups
warm water
plastic spoon
plastic bowl
stopwatch

Think It Over

1. Use the data you collected to draw conclusions about which dissolves faster, a whole antacid tablet or one that is ground up. Do the results agree or disagree with your hypothesis?

   _____

2. What variable affected how long it took each tablet to dissolve completely?

   _____

3. How are your results similar to what happens to weathered rock?

   _____

ROCKS AND WEATHERING

Quick Lab   10 min

Freezing and Thawing

Water is an important force of mechanical weathering, especially when it freezes. In this activity, you will investigate how ice helps to break down rock.

INQUIRY FOCUS Observe

Procedure

1. 🧤 Put on your safety goggles. Obtain three samples of sandstone from your teacher. Examine them with the magnifying (hand) lens. Pay special attention to any individual grains you can see.

2. Place two rocks in the plastic cup. Fill the cup with enough water to cover the rocks. Place both the cup and the dry rock in the place designated by your teacher and leave them overnight.

3. The next day, carefully pour the water out of the cup. Label a plastic bag "Soaked rock," a second plastic bag "Soaked rock—freezer." and a third plastic bag "Dry rock." Place the soaked rocks inside separate plastic bags and seal them. Place the dry rock inside the third plastic bag and seal it.

4. Place the dry rock and the rock labeled "Soaked rock—freezer" in a freezer overnight. Place the other soaked rock in the place designated by your teacher.

5. On the third day, remove the rocks from the freezer. On a white sheet of paper, write the labels of all three bags. Take all three rocks out of their plastic bags and place them on the paper at their correct labels . Observe the surface of the rocks with the magnifying (hand) lens. Pay special attention to any individual grains you can see. Rub a finger over the rocks in the same way. In Question 1 below, note what you observe. Examine the inside of each plastic bag. Again, note what you observe.

Materials

- 3 sandstone rock samples
- magnifying (hand) lens
- plastic cup
- water
- 3 plastic bags
- marking pen
- a freezer
- white sheet of paper

Think It Over

1 Describe your observations of each rock before and after freezing. Pay special attention to individual grains.

_____

_____

2 What is responsible for the differences you observed?

_____

_____

Quick Lab 5 min

Rusting Away

Rust is a product of chemical weathering. It forms when iron metal that is often present in rock combines with oxygen in the air in a process called oxidation.

INQUIRY FOCUS Predict

Procedure

1. Obtain a new piece of steel wool from your teacher, and observe its structure.

2. With the dropper, put several drops of water from the cup onto the steel wool to moisten it. Place the steel wool in the bag. Seal the bag completely so the steel wool will not dry out. Set the bag aside for three days. Predict what will happen to the steel wool in the bag.

_____

3. After three days, observe the steel wool in the bag.

4. 🥽 🧤 ✂️ Put on your goggles and gloves. Obtain another new piece of steel wool and squeeze it between your fingers. Then remove the steel wool from the bag and squeeze it between your fingers.

> **Materials**
>
> 2 pieces of steel wool
> plastic cup
> dropper
> plastic resealable bag

Think It Over

1 What happened to the steel wool after three days? Does this match your prediction?

_____

2 Describe what happened when you squeezed the second, new piece of steel wool between your fingers. What happened when you squeezed the steel wool that was in the bag?

_____

_____

3 This is the same process of oxidation that weathers rock. Explain how this process would break down rock.

_____

Name _____ Date_____ Class_____

_____

It's All on the Surface

Various factors determine how quickly weathering occurs. In this activity, you will explore one way to speed up the weathering process.

Procedure

1. In this investigation, the soap represents rock. The process of dissolving the soap represents weathering. With your partner, write a hypothesis about the relationship between water temperature and weathering.

   _____

2. Use the wax pencil to label one cup cold water, another cup room temperature water, and the third cup hot tap water. Fill each cup with 150 mL of the appropriate temperature water.

3. Have one lab partner start the stopwatch at the same time another lab partner drops one piece of soap into each cup.

4. Carefully look at the soap and note your observations. After 5 minutes have passed, observe the cups again and note any changes to the soap. Wait another 5 minutes and observe the cups again.

5. Pour out the water and use the plastic spoon to pluck the soap out of the cup onto a paper towel. Pick up the soap. How do the pieces compare?

Materials

3 pieces of soap
3 plastic cups
cold water
room temperature water
hot tap water
wax pencil
plastic spoon
stopwatch or clock
paper towel

Think It Over

1 In which cup did the soap dissolve the most?

_____

2 What do the results of this activity tell you about conditions that help speed up the dissolving rate?

_____

3 How could these results help you infer the rate of weathering of rock in different climates?

_____

Inquiry Warm-Up ●————— 15 min

What Is Soil?

Soil is made up of loose, weathered material on Earth's surface. In this activity, you will explore the components that make up soil.

INQUIRY FOCUS Form an Operational Definition

Procedure

1. 🧤 Put on your safety goggles.

2. Obtain a soil sample from your teacher. Use the toothpick to separate the soil into individual particles.

3. With the magnifying lens, try to identify the different types of particles in the sample. Record your answers.

   _____

   _____

Materials

soil sample on paper
   plate
toothpick
magnifying lens
paper
pencil

4. Return the soil sample to the place designated by your teacher. Wash your hands when you are finished.

Think It Over

1 Based on your observations, what would be your operational definition for soil? *Hint: Remember that an operational definition is based on what you can observe.*

_____

_____

_____

2 Write a "recipe" for the sample of soil, naming each of the "ingredients" that you think the soil contains. Include what percentage of each ingredient would be needed if someone were to use your recipe to make soil. Compare your recipe with those of your classmates.

_____

_____

_____

● **Lab Investigation**

PRE LAB

Investigating Soils and Drainage

Reviewing Content

One property scientists use to classify soil is permeability, or the ability of water to drain through soil. The permeability of soil depends largely on its texture, or the size of the particles that compose it.

There are three major soil particle sizes. Sand particles are the largest, and produce coarse or grainy soils. Clay particles are the smallest, and produce smooth, heavy soils. Silt particles are between the size of sand and clay. Each type of soil is largely a mixture of these three types of particles.

Because soil drainage affects the growth of plants, farmers must be aware of the texture of their soil. Sandy soil has a coarse texture because its particles and the pore spaces between them are fairly large. Sandy soils are very permeable. This allows water to drain quickly through. These soils can drain so quickly that plants growing in sandy soils can die for lack of water. Clay soils are dense and heavy because clay particles and the spaces between them are tiny. Clay soils are not very permeable and can become soggy because they retain water. Plants that grow in clay soils can drown in the water-logged soil.

Reviewing Inquiry Focus

Make Models When you make a model, you create a mental or physical representation of a process that often cannot be seen. In some cases, the process takes place over such a long period of time that it would be impossible to observe. For example, you might make a model of the way a river carves out a canyon because the actual process can take thousands of years or more. Scientists also make models to show objects or processes that the unaided eye can't see. When you make a model, you observe the way it works and use it to gather both qualitative and quantitative data. Qualitative data are observations about an item that cannot be measured, such as its color, feel, or smell. Quantitative data are measurements scientists make using tools such as rulers, scales, or timers.

1 What will you be modeling during this investigation?

_____

_____

2 Will you collect qualitative or quantitative data in this investigation? Explain.

_____

_____

HOW SOIL FORMS

DIRECTED Inquiry • 35 min

Investigating Soils and Drainag

Problem

How fast does water drain through different types of soil?

Materials

4 plastic 2-liter bottles with 1/3 of the bottom cut off

4 plastic 2-liter bottles with 1/3 of the top cut off and a hole punched in their side

4 pieces of gauze or cheesecloth (about 8 cm × 8 cm)

4 rubber bands

Soil Sample 1, potting soil

Soil Sample 2, sand

Soil Sample 3, clay mixed with soil

Soil Sample 4, gravel mixed with soil

plastic pitcher, at least 1-liter

timer or watch

permanent marker or wax pencil

100-mL graduated cylinder or metric measuring cup

Procedure

1. Obtain your set of plastic bottles from your teacher.

2. 🥽 🦺 Put on your goggles and lab apron. Cover the spout of each bottle that has its bottom cut off with a piece of gauze or cheesecloth. Secure the cheesecloth on each bottle with a rubber band.

3. You will make four setups, as follows. Invert a bottle with a covered spout and fill it halfway with Soil Sample 1, potting soil. Label the bottle with the correct soil sample number.

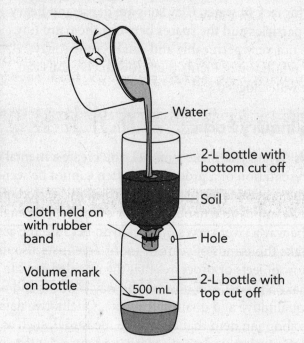

Water

2-L bottle with bottom cut off

Soil

Cloth held on with rubber band

Hole

Volume mark on bottle

500 mL

2-L bottle with top cut off

—————————————— **DIRECTED** Inquiry —————— • **Lab Investigation**

**INVESTIGATING SOILS
AND DRAINAGE** *continued*

4. Place the bottle containing the soil over an empty bottle with no top. Refer to the diagram of the setup on the previous page.

5. Repeat Steps 3 and 4 for the remaining bottles and soil samples.

6. You are now ready to test your soil samples. As you complete the investigation, fill in the first column of the data table below with the name of each soil type and record draining time data in the second column. Predict which soil will drain most slowly and which soil will drain most quickly. Give reasons for your predictions.

_____

_____

7. Fill the graduated cylinder or measuring cup with 100 mL of water. Start timing the moment you pour water from the cylinder or measuring cup into the soil. Measure the amount of time it takes from when you start pouring until you see the first drips in the bottom bottle. *Note: You will need to refill the graduated cylinder, possibly more than once.* Once the water starts to drip through, put the setup aside and record your data in the table.

8. Repeat Step 7 with the remaining soil samples. Be sure to use the same amount of water for each trial.

9. 🖐 Clean up and dispose of your samples as directed by your teacher. Wash your hands with warm water and soap when you finish handling soil.

Data Table

Soil Type	Draining Time

DIRECTED Inquiry ●—— Lab Investigation

**INVESTIGATING SOILS
AND DRAINAGE** continued

Analyze and Conclude

1 **Make Models** Through which soil did water drain the fastest?
The slowest?

_____

_____

2 **Infer** What happens to the water from the time you pour it into the
soil until the time it drains into the plastic bottle?

_____

_____

_____

3 **Draw Conclusions** Why did the water drain through the soil at
different rates?

_____

_____

_____

4 **Predict** If you waited until water stopped draining from all the soils,
would the same amount of water have drained into each holding
container? Explain.

_____

_____

5 **Develop a Hypothesis** Based on your observations and study of the
chapter, form a hypothesis about which type of soil would be best for a
garden bed holding plants that do not grow well in very moist soil.
Would the best type of soil be sand or clay? Explain.

_____

_____

_____

HOW SOIL FORMS

Name _____ Date _____ Class _____

POST LAB

Investigating Soils and Drainage

1 **Interpret Data** Did your results agree with your predictions? If they did not, explain why you think they did not agree.

_____

_____

_____

_____

2 **Design an Experiment** If you wanted to extend the investigation and test other soils, how might you change your procedure?

_____

_____

_____

_____

3 **Summarize** State what you learned in this investigation about the relationship between particle size of soil and drainage.

What I learned _____

_____

_____

_____

What I still want to know _____

_____

_____

_____

Communicate

Critique Scientific Explanations and Models Did you encounter any problems while making your model and while carrying out the investigation? Write a list of tips you would give other students that would help them carry it out with fewer problems.

HOW SOIL FORMS

OPEN Inquiry • 35 min

Investigating Soils and Drainag

Problem

How fast does water drain through different types of soil?

INQUIRY FOCUS
Observe, Measure,
Design an Experiment

Materials

4 plastic 2-L
    soft-drink bottles
    with bottoms
    removed

4 plastic 2-L
    soft-drink bottles
    with tops cut
    off and a hole
    punched in the
    side

4 pieces of gauze or
    cheesecloth, about
    8 cm × 8 cm

4 rubber bands

potting soil

sand

clay mixed with soil

gravel mixed with
    soil

1-L plastic container

timer or watch

permanent marker
    or wax pencil

graduated cylinder
    or metric
    measuring cup
    (100 mL)

beakers

apron and goggles

Design an Experiment

1. Almost all of Earth's water—97 percent—is contained in the oceans, and another two percent is bound up in ice. Only one percent of water on Earth is available fresh water. Most of that fresh water is groundwater, which is all the water contained in spaces within bedrock and soil.

2. Whether soil is composed of coarse pieces of rock or very fine particles, there is always some space between the pieces of solid material. This space is called *pore space*. The amount of water that material can hold is determined by a property called *porosity*. Porosity is simply the percentage of the total volume of bedrock or soil that consists of open spaces, or pores. Porosity is affected by the grain sizes of the particles making up the rock or soil, the grain size distribution, and the amount of cementing materials binding the grains together.

3. When experimenting with how water flows through rock or soil, permeability is another important factor to consider. Permeability is a measure of how connected the pore spaces are. We can measure permeability by determining how fast water flows through a material.

a. In your own words, what does *porosity* mean? (Draw a picture if it helps.)

    _____

    _____

    Name one type of porous material: _____

b. In your own words, what does *permeability* mean? (Draw a picture if it helps.)

    Name one type of permeable material: _____

    _____

    _____

OPEN Inquiry ————————• **Lab Investigation**

**INVESTIGATING SOILS
AND DRAINAGE** *continued*

4. Both porosity and permeability affect how fast water flows through the ground. You will be designing an experiment to test water flow through different Earth materials. You will use the materials to create an apparatus that will allow you to compare how quickly water flows through different soils. Use the space provided below to sketch your apparatus.

5. Develop a testable hypothesis about how the composition and porosity of a particular soil affects how quickly water will drip or flow through a column of soil (the soil's permeability). Write your hypothesis in an "if, then" format.

_____

_____

6.  Plan the procedure you will follow for your experiment. Write it on a separate sheet of paper.

7. Design a data table to record your observations. Be sure to identify what you are measuring, the units you are using and what variables you are testing.

8. Have your teacher approve your design, procedure, hypothesis, and data table. Then, carry out your experiment.

Sketch

Data Table

HOW SOIL FORMS

Name _____ Date_____ Class_____

INVESTIGATING SOILS
AND DRAINAGE *continued*

Analyze and Conclude:

1 **Measure** Which material has the highest permeability?

_____

_____

2 **Analyze Experimental Results** How does the permeability vary with
the size of the material's particles?

_____

_____

_____

3 **Interpret Data** Why do different materials have different
permeabilities?

_____

_____

_____

4 **Infer** What would be an agricultural disadvantage if a farmer's fields
had soil with high permeability?

_____

_____

_____

5 **Draw Conclusions** Why do parking lots tend to have a large number of
puddles after a rain?

_____

_____

OPEN Inquiry ————————————— • Lab Investigation

POST LAB

Investigating Soils and Drainage

1 **Design an Experiment** What sources of error that might affect the results might be encountered in this activity?

_____

_____

_____

2 **Draw Conclusions** Can you accept or reject your hypothesis? Why or why not?

_____

_____

_____

3 **Summarize** State what you learned in this investigation about the relationship between particle size of soil and drainage.

What I learned _____

_____

_____

_____

What I still want to know _____

_____

_____

_____

Communicate

Make a *brief* presentation of your findings to the class that includes the following:

a. State your group's hypothesis (1 sentence)

b. Briefly describe your experiment (2–3 sentences)

c. Show your resulting data (1–2 sentences)

d. State whether your hypothesis was correct or not (1 sentence)

e. Explain anything that you would do differently if you were to repeat your experiment (1–2 sentences)

f. Explain how porosity and permeability contribute to the process of breaking down rock into soil. (2–3 sentences)

HOW SOIL FORMS

Name _____ Date_____ Class_____

Quick Lab   15 min

The Contents of Soil

Soil is a mixture of rock particles, minerals, air, water, and organic matter such as decaying plants and animals. In this activity, you will examine a soil sample to classify the materials you find within it.

INQUIRY FOCUS Classify

Procedure

1. Put on your safety goggles. Pour a soil sample on to your tray. Use the craft sticks, toothpicks, and tweezers to help move the soil around and separate out the different materials in it. Look for rock and mineral particles, organic material, and anything else that can be identified as a component of the soil.

2. Use the spoon to move the contents of the soil into three categories: organic, inorganic, and unknown.

3. With your partner, try to identify and list the materials you have classified in each category. Use a hand lens to help you. Record your lists of materials in the data table below.

4. When you are finished, return your soil sample to the place designated by your teacher. Wash your hands again.

Materials

- soil sample
- plastic spoon
- toothpicks
- craft sticks
- tweezers
- hand lens
- pencil
- plastic tray

Contents of Soil		
Organic	**Inorganic**	**Unknown**

Think It Over

1. List at least one substance you observed in each category.

_____

_____

2. What is the source of the organic material in the soil? How do you think it got there?

_____

_____

52

HOW SOIL FORMS

Copyright © Pearson Education, Inc., or its affiliates. All rights reserved.

Inquiry Warm-Up ● 15 min

How Can You Keep Soil From Washing Away?

Fertile soil is a valuable resource because every organism on land depends on it. Because soil takes a long time to form, soil conservation is important. In this activity, you will explore ways to keep soil from washing away.

INQUIRY FOCUS Observe

Procedure

1. Put on your goggles. Measure about 550 mL of soil into the larger beaker, then pour it onto the pie plate. Mound it into the shape of a hill.

2. Design and carry out a procedure to keep the soil from washing away when water is poured over it. To protect the pile of soil, you may use craft sticks, paper clips, pebbles, modeling clay, strips of paper, or other materials approved by your teacher.

3. Fill the smaller beaker with 200 mL of water. Hold the beaker about 20 cm above the center of the soil, and slowly pour the water in a stream onto the soil.

4. Observe the hill. Compare the hill in your pan of soil with the hills of your classmates.

5. Place the soil and the assorted objects in the place designated by your teacher. Wash your hands.

Materials

- soil
- 1000-mL beaker
- 250-mL beaker
- metal pie plate
- craft sticks
- paper clips
- pebbles
- modeling clay
- strips of paper
- water
- ruler

Think It Over

1 Based on observations of your hill and those of your classmates, what do you think is the best way to prevent soil on a slope from washing away?

_____

_____

_____

2 What made the most successful arrangements work as well as they did?

_____

_____

_____

SOIL CONSERVATION

Quick Lab   15 min

Using It Up

Fertile soil is rich in the nutrients plants need to grow. Plants take in those nutrients from the soil through their roots. In this activity, you will investigate how water and nutrients travel from soil through plants.

INQUIRY FOCUS Predict

Procedure

1. Put on an apron. Fill each beaker with 200 mL of water.

2. Put 10 drops of food coloring into the water in one beaker. Stir the water to mix the food coloring well. The food coloring represents nutrients in soil.

3. Obtain a flower with a split stem from your teacher. With the two beakers right next to each other, position the flower so that one half of the split stem is in the beaker with colored water. The other half of the stem should be in the beaker with plain water. Place a small object, such as an opened book, next to the beakers and lean the top of the flower against it for support. Predict what will happen to the flower during the next few hours.

_____

4. The next day, observe the stem and petals of the flower with the hand lens. Be sure to look only at the portions of the stems that were above the water level.

Materials

two 250-mL beakers
water
food coloring
plastic spoon
flower with split stem
hand lens

Think It Over

1. What did you observe in the flower? Did your observations agree with your prediction? Explain.

_____

2. Based on your observations, how did the "nutrients" get into the flower? How is this similar to what happens to plants growing in soil?

_____

3. Using the results of this investigation as a guide, explain how plants can contribute to a loss of nutrients in soil.

_____

SOIL CONSERVATION

Name _____ Date _____ Class _____

Soil Conservation

Farmers concerned about erosion use several methods to conserve soil, such as contour plowing and terracing. In this activity, you will model contour plowing and terracing, and predict their effect on soil erosion.

INQUIRY FOCUS Predict

Procedure

Materials

- mixture of damp soil and sand
- empty aquarium
- plastic knife
- small soda bottle with cap containing small holes
- water
- meter stick

1. 🌀 🛡 Put on your safety goggles and apron. Get enough sand and soil mixture from your teacher to make a mound in the center of the aquarium. Your teacher will tell you to model either contour plowing, terracing, or plowing without conservation measures to determine the amount of erosion.

2. **To model contour plowing:** Use the plastic knife to make small grooves in the mound across the slope of the hill. **To model terracing:** Build several leveled areas, like steps, up the sides of the hill. **To model plowing without conservation measures:** Use the plastic knife to make small grooves running straight up and down the slope of the hill.

3. Predict how water sprinkled on the hill will drain from it. Will a large amount of soil erode from your hill? Why or why not?

_____

4. Fill the soda bottle with water, and put on the cap. Then, holding it upside down about 1 meter above the top of the hill, sprinkle water gently over the very top of the hill. Do not move the bottle around the hill. Observe the results.

5. 🗑 🧼 Clean up your lab materials and dispose of them in the place designated by your teacher. Wash your hands with warm water and soap.

Think It Over

1 Did you correctly predict how the water would drain from your hill? If not, why was your prediction wrong?

_____

2 Give an explanation for the amount of erosion you observed on your hill. How did the method of preparing the land increase or decrease erosion?

_____

Erosion and Deposition

Mass Movement

❓ Answering the Big Question

The activities in this lesson will help students answer the Big Question by examining the movement of objects and sediment down slopes to understand conditions that result in mass movement, exploring factors that affect the rate of erosion, and understanding how stable landforms are created.

How Does Gravity Affect Materials on a Slope?

Inquiry Focus

Develop a Hypothesis—making a testable statement that explains how gravity affects materials that move down a slope

Group Size Pairs

Class Time 15 minutes

Safety

Caution students to watch for marbles on the floor that might have rolled off the desks unnoticed.

Advance Preparation (15 minutes)

Precut sandpaper to sizes that can be wrapped around the board and the block of wood. The block of wood should be completely wrapped in sandpaper. The board does not have to be completely covered if there is enough overlap.

Answers

1. Sample Answer: Upon lifting the board, all of the objects moved downhill with gravity. The marble immediately rolled down the slope. The block of wood slid down as well, but only when the board was lifted higher. When the block of wood and the board were covered with sandpaper, the block did not move until the board was lifted up almost vertically.

2. Look for hypotheses stating that while all materials moved downslope with gravity, the resistance of friction (with the block of wood and even more so with the sandpaper) made movement downhill more difficult and required steeper slopes.

3. The newscaster is stating an opinion because the claim is not founded in scientific evidence. Heavy rainfall is a possible cause of mudflow, but does not mean that the mudflows are imminent. The newscaster should have considered the location of any hills, the composition of the soil, and the presence of foliage.

Quick Lab

Weathering and Erosion

🔑 Unlocking the Key Concept

This lab will help students understand the effects of water and slope angle on the rate of erosion.

Inquiry Focus

Make Models—modeling wet and dry conditions on a slope to help students conceptualize how erosion takes place

Group Size Groups

Class Time 20 minutes

Safety

1. Students should wear their goggles and aprons throughout this exercise.

2. Students should wash their hands when they complete their work.

Alternative Materials

Any dry soil may be used, including sand. Any container that will hold the soil can be used for mixing. A large baking pan can also be used in place of a tray.

Procedure Tips

1. Display a data table for students to record their observations. Have them copy it on a separate sheet of paper. See the sample data table below.

	Dry Soil	Wet Soil
1st angle (___ degrees)		
2nd angle (___ degrees)		

2. In Step 3 students may need you to model how to hold the protractor to measure the angle of the board.

Answers
1. Sample Answer: The soil that had the most water in it moved the most down the slope.
2. Sample Answer: At a lower angle, the soil took longer to move down the board. But at a steeper angle, the soil moved more quickly.

Lab Investigation

Sand Hills

🔑 Unlocking the Key Concept

Directed Inquiry This activity will help students form sand hills and describe the height-to-width ratio that creates a stable landform, one that is least subject to mass movement.

Open Inquiry This activity will reinforce the idea that the steepness of a hill is determined in large part by its material composition.

Answers—Pre Lab
Both Versions:
1. Sample Answer: You could use a ruler to make actual measurements.
2. Look for answers that suggest that letting the hill form on its own allows the sand to settle into its most stable structure.

Inquiry Focus
Both Versions:
Develop a Hypothesis—using observations to develop a possible explanation for the relationship between sand hill height and width
Interpret Data—analyzing data about sand hill height and width to identify patterns to test the hypothesis
Graph—organizing data in a visual way to show the relationship between height and width of a sand hill

Group Size
Directed Inquiry Groups
Open Inquiry Pairs

Class Time
Both Versions 40 minutes

Safety
Both Versions:
1. Students should wear goggles throughout this lab.
2. Students should wash their hands upon completion of the activity.

Advance Preparation (40 minutes)
Both Versions:
1. Collect cardboard tubes and cardboard box-tops or plastic trays in advance.
2. Make sure the sand is dry.
3. If sand is limited in supply, you might tell students to recycle their own sand by using a funneling device to pour it from the tray back into the container. If butcher paper is used, sand could be carefully poured back into the container by lifting the paper at its sides.

Alternative Materials
Both Versions:
Butcher block paper cut to fit the tray bottom can be used instead of taping smaller sheets together. Butcher paper can be cut to fit the trays more precisely, but 1-cm grid paper allows for easier student set-up of hill width scales. Fine aquarium gravel can be used instead of sand. Cardboard tubes from rolls of toilet tissue are an appropriate size for this activity.

Procedure Tips
Directed Inquiry:
1. Give students time to read through the procedure and then ask: **What are some possible relationships between the height of the sand hill and the width of the sand hill?** *(The height could be greater than the width or vice versa. The ratio between height and width might be the same for all sizes of sand hills, or it might be different.)* Guide students to develop a specific hypothesis that can be tested. Sample Hypothesis: The ratio of the sand hill's height to its width always remains the same. Allow students to test any reasonable hypothesis.
2. Caution students not to touch the sand hill as it is forming, but to allow the sand hill to form on its own as the sand falls from the tube.

Open Inquiry:
1. Focus on the development of hypotheses. Ask, **What is a hypothesis, and what do we do with it?** *(A hypothesis is a proposed explanation for an observation in the form of a statement that can be tested by scientific experimentation. We test a hypothesis.)* Ask, **If you compare the height of a hill at its peak with the width at its base, what relationship do you see?** *(Look for answers that*

EROSION AND DEPOSITION

indicate that students understand the ratio of height to width.) Ask, **What determines this relationship?** *(the type of material composing the hill.)* Ask, **What types of material would form hills that are wider than they are tall? Taller than they are wide?** *(Sample answer: Fine materials would form broad hills, whereas larger or stickier materials might form tall hills.)*

2. Distribute the materials and allow students five minutes to come up with their experimental designs. Look over their procedures and offer guidance before letting them proceed with the tests of their hypotheses. If students want to adjust a variable, make some suggestions such as:

   - dropping the sand onto an existing hill and measuring height and width with each sequential deposit of sand
   - dropping different volumes of sand
   - dropping sand from different heights

3. Sample Answer to Procedure Step 1: The width of my sand hill was greater than the height.

4. Sample Hypothesis for Procedure Step 2: If sand is added to a sand hill, the width of the sand hill will increase faster than its height.

Answers—Analyze and Conclude
Directed Inquiry:

1. A typical graph should show a line rising from left to right. If width is on the *x*-axis and height is on the *y*-axis, the slope of the line should be about $\frac{1}{3}$. However, this value can vary slightly.

2. Sample Answer: The ratio between height and width remains about the same regardless of the size of the hill.

3. Look for answers in which students compare their original hypothesis with the data collected.

4. Advise students who proposed a hypothesis that was not supported to develop a new hypothesis that is consistent with the data collected.

Open Inquiry:

1. Sample Answer: The relationship between sand hill height and width remains relatively constant, even when new sand is dropped on top of the existing hill. This confirmed my hypothesis.

2. Sample Answer: I noticed that as the height of the hill increased, the width increased twice as much.

3. Look for answers indicating that gravity is pulling the sand down. Friction keeps some of the sand in place, allowing the hill to have some height.

4. Sample Answer: I would compare the height-to-width relationship in sand hills of different water contents, such as dry sand, damp sand, damper sand, and very wet sand.

Answers—Post Lab
Directed Inquiry:

1. Students should predict that the ratio of height to width would remain approximately the same. They could test their prediction by making and measuring five more sand hills.

2. Sample Answer: Using wet sand will produce hills that stand at a higher angle (larger height-to-width ratio). Using larger sediment, such as gravel, also will produce hills that stand at a higher angle.

3. Look for answers that incorporate the height-to-width ratio students calculated, or that describe a common structure (e.g., base twice as wide as height).

4. Students should infer that mass movement is more likely on slopes that are steep.

5. Sample Answer: I learned that the ratio between height and width remains about the same regardless of the size of the hill. I want to know if the ratio would change if the hill was made of a different material.

Communicate—Sample Answer: Disturbing the sand hills while taking measurements affected results.

Open Inquiry:

1. Sample Answer: It was difficult to measure the hill height without disturbing the sand at the top of the hill and taking away some of its height. Measuring the height more carefully might help prevent this problem.

2. Look for answers that suggest that rain could erode the materials of the hill, making it shorter and broader over time, or it could strengthen the hill by providing moisture that makes the materials stick together. Wind might take material away, but it might also push the hill to higher heights or different shapes, as in sand dunes. Snow or freezing

temperatures could preserve the shape of the hill by packing down water-saturated soils. Earthquakes could shake layers loose, causing large landslides.

3. Sample Answer: The truck loaded with sand would probably cause a bigger problem because the fine sand is more likely to spill across a wider area than the larger, heavier rocks.

4. Sample Answer: I learned that the ratio between height and width remains about the same regardless of the size of the hill. I want to know if the ratio would change if the hill was made of a different material.

Communicate—Look for answers that include three different hillside compositions and the long-term stability of each and why each is stable or unstable, or why each is likely or unlikely to be affected by weather, erosion, and/or landslides. The composition, safety, and risks of each hillside should be detailed and illustrated with accuracy in a format suitable for a presentation.

Water Erosion

Answering the Big Question

The activities in this lesson will help students answer the Big Question by modeling erosion caused by running water and rain and by modeling how groundwater forms limestone caverns.

How Does Moving Water Wear Away Rocks?

Inquiry Focus

Predict—making an educated guess about how water dripping from a faucet will wear away soap and how this models the way water erodes rock

Group Size Groups

Class Time 15 minutes

Safety

Warn students to immediately wipe up any spills that occur in the lab area.

Procedure Tips

Before students conduct the experiment, have them read through the procedure and identify both the variable that is being tested (dripping water) and the control (the bar kept in a dry place).

Answers

1. Sample Answer: I predicted that the dripping water will wear a depression in the bar of soap.

2. Sample Answer: The depression in the soap would be larger after an additional 10 minutes, and even larger after an hour. Increasing the flow would speed up the process, while decreasing the flow would slow down the process.

3. Look for answers that suggest that the drip of water slowly wears away the soap as falling or moving water slowly wears away rock.

Raindrops Falling

Unlocking the Key Concept

This activity will allow students to model rain dropping on soil to determine how this contributes to water erosion.

Inquiry Focus

Draw Conclusions—using a model to determine the way falling drops of rain erode soil

Group Size Pairs

Class Time 15 minutes

Safety

1. Students should wear safety goggles and lab aprons throughout this activity.

2. Warn students to immediately wipe up any water that spills in the lab area.

Procedure Tips

To drop water from a height of 2 m, students will have to place the petri dish on the floor and hold the dropper above their heads. An alternative is to reduce the distance to 0.5 m in the first set of trials and then 1 m in the second set of trials.

Answers

1. Sample Answer: The drops from 2 m will produce bigger splashes that travel farther than the drops from 1 m. Because the drops move sediment when they hit the soil, the 2 m drops will cause more erosion. The 2 m drops have more kinetic energy because the water falls from a greater distance.

2. Look for answers that suggest heavier rainfall, or larger raindrops, rather than a light shower, would cause the most erosion.

Erosion Cube

🗝 Unlocking the Key Concept

This activity will allow students to use sugar cubes and water to model and observe groundwater erosion.

Inquiry Focus

Observe—using the visual senses to determine how groundwater can erode rock underground

Group Size Groups

Class Time 15 minutes

Safety

1. Warn students to immediately wipe up any water that spills in the lab area.

2. Students should not taste or eat any of the sugar cubes.

Answers

1. Students will observe that some of the sugar from the large block dissolved in water from the paper towel, leaving the block smaller and misshapen.

2. Sample Answer: This is similar to water seeping through cracks in limestone, eroding the rock, and then carrying the material away in solution.

Glacial Erosion

❓ Answering the Big Question

The activities in this lesson will help students answer the Big Question by modeling the way glaciers scour the ground, by modeling conditions that cause a glacier to surge, and by modeling how glacial erosion reshapes valleys.

How Do Glaciers Change the Land?

Inquiry Focus

Infer—suggesting how sand frozen into the bottom of an ice cube and scraped over a piece of soap models the way glaciers change the land as they move over it

Group Size Pairs

Class Time 10 minutes, plus 5 minutes the next day

Safety

Students should wear their goggles throughout this activity.

Procedure Tips

1. If you do not freeze the water overnight, make sure the cups are kept in the freezer long enough for the ice to freeze completely.

2. Tell students to rub the ice in one direction only, just as a glacier would move.

3. Be sure students do not fill the cup to the top with water; it will expand and overflow when it freezes.

Answers

1. The sediment on the bottom of the ice scrapes away the surface of the soap.

2. Sample Answer: The sediment embedded in the ice scratches and scrapes the soap in the same way that rock embedded in a moving glacier scratches and scrapes the land under it.

Surging Glaciers

🗝 Unlocking the Key Concept

This activity will help students model the conditions that cause a glacier to surge.

Inquiry Focus

Observe—using the visual senses to determine how the movement of a lid across a floor changes when a dry floor is covered with drops of water, and relating this to movement of a surging glacier

Group Size Groups

Class Time 5 minutes

Safety

Tell students to avoid stepping in areas where the floor is wet. Students should wipe up the water immediately after finishing the lab.

Advance Preparation (10 minutes)

Find an out-of-the-way area of the school or classroom for this activity.

Answers

1. Sample Answer: The lid slides across the wet floor more easily, because the layer of water between the lid and the floor reduces friction between the lid and the floor.
2. Sample Answer: Glaciers can surge when a layer of water or wet mud gets between the glacier and the rock below it. This is similar to placing a layer of water between the lid and the floor.

Quick Lab

Modeling Valleys

🔑 Unlocking the Key Concept

This activity will allow students to model the erosion that forms V-shaped and U-shaped valleys.

Inquiry Focus

Make a Model—making and contrasting a physical representation of a valley eroded by a stream and a valley eroded by a glacier

Group Size Groups

Class Time 20 minutes

Advance Preparation (30 minutes)

1. Freeze enough ice cubes so that each group has one.
2. To save time, set up the stream table with soil before class.

Alternative Materials

Sand can be substituted for the soil. Large plastic "sweater boxes" with drainage holes and hoses connected to the faucet and run to the boxes can be substituted for the stream tables.

Safety

1. Warn students to immediately wipe up any spills that occur in the lab area.
2. Students should wear their goggles and aprons throughout the activity.

Answers

1. Stream-formed valleys have a V shape, while glacier-formed valleys have a U shape.
2. Sample Answer: Geologists could determine areas that were covered by glaciers during the last ice age by identifying areas with U-shaped valleys.

Wave Erosion

❓ Answering the Big Question

The activities in this lesson will help students answer the Big Question as they study the different characteristics of beach sand and the erosive effect that waves have on a beach.

Inquiry Warm-Up

What Is Sand Made Of?

Inquiry Focus

Pose Questions—stating a problem in a way that allows students to think about and try to determine the answers to questions about the origin of beach sand

Group Size Individuals

Class Time 15 minutes

Safety

1. Students should wear goggles throughout this activity.
2. They should wash their hands when finished with the lab.

Advance Preparation

Label each sand container as follows: Beach Sand #1, Beach Sand #2, and so on. Only two samples are needed for this activity, but you might wish to provide more to stress the large variation in sand characteristics.

Alternative Materials

If sand is not available locally from a nearby lake or ocean beach, substitute two types of commercial sand.

Procedure Tips

To make sure that students do not mix the samples, provide only one sample at a time for examination.

Answers

1. Sample Answer: Is beach sand the result of erosion? How is beach sand deposited? What causes the difference in the beach sand from various places?

2. Look for answers that include descriptions of grain size, shape, color, and so on.

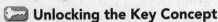

Shaping a Coastline

Unlocking the Key Concept

This activity will help students understand the relationship between wave impact and erosion along a shoreline.

Inquiry Focus

Control Variables—investigating the direction and force of waves as they approach shore and observing how a combination of variables determines shoreline erosion

Group Size Pairs

Class Time 15 minutes

Safety

1. Students should wear their safety goggles throughout the activity.

2. Tell students to clean up spills, both water and sand, promptly.

Procedure Tips

1. Use pencils with 6-sided wooden barrels to prevent rolling under the pan.

2. Tell students to record the variable they change, such as the wave size or wave direction, and record their observations in their notebooks. Make sure they do this for each variable they change.

Answers

1. Sample Answer: The direct waves made the beach steeper because sand was carried out into the water. The sand was moved away from the end of the beach where the angled wave hit first and deposited along the farther end.

2. Look for answers stating that the sand washed out from under the rocks, exposing the rocks more.

3. Sample Answer: You could increase the wave size, change the frequency of the waves to mimic stormy conditions, or change the shape of the beach.

Wind Erosion

Answering the Big Question

The activities in this lesson will help students answer the Big Question by having them model how wind erodes sediment and forms desert pavement.

How Does Moving Air Affect Sediment?

Inquiry Focus

Observe—using the visual senses to determine how air blown through a straw over cornmeal models the way wind erodes sediment

Group Size Pairs

Class Time 10 minutes

Safety

1. Students must wear their safety goggles throughout this entire activity.

2. Caution students to avoid blowing the cornmeal in the direction of another student.

3. Have students clean up any cornmeal that blows out of the pan.

4. Students who have grain allergies should not do this lab.

Procedure Tips

Emphasize that students should blow gently through the straw.

Answers

1. Students should observe that blowing gently through the straw eroded cornmeal from some places.

2. Wind moves sediment on Earth's surface the way blown air moves cornmeal in this activity.

Quick Lab

Desert Pavement

🔑 Unlocking the Key Concept

This activity will allow students to model the formation of desert pavement, a product of wind erosion.

Inquiry Focus

Make a Model—making a physical representation of the formation of desert pavement, using moving air blown over a pan of coins covered with flour

Group Size Groups

Class Time 10 minutes

Safety

1. Students should wear their safety goggles and aprons throughout the entire activity.
2. Caution students not to draw in any flour through the straw.
3. Students with grain allergies should not do this activity.

Answers

1. The "wind" removed flour from around and on top of the coins.
2. Students should realize that the longer they blow, the more flour will be removed from the pan. Blowing long enough would remove most, if not all, of the flour.
3. Sample Answer: The lab setup models wind removing sand from around rocks to create a desert pavement. The coins represent the rocks, and the flour represents the sand around them.

How Does Gravity Affect Materials on a Slope?

All materials move downhill with gravity. But does the effect of gravity change with the type of material, or the conditions on the slope? In this activity, you will develop a hypothesis to examine these questions.

INQUIRY FOCUS Develop a Hypothesis

Procedure

1. Place a small board flat on your desk. Place a marble on the board and slowly lift one end of the board. Observe what happens to the marble.

2. Place a block of wood on the board. Again, slowly lift one end of the board. Observe the effect on the block of wood, and compare the amount of lifting needed to move the marble and the wood.

3. Last, cover the board and the wood block with sandpaper. Tape the sandpaper closed, and repeat Step 2. Again, note the amount of lifting needed to move the block of wood.

4. Develop a hypothesis to explain your observations.

Materials

small board
marble
block of wood
sandpaper
tape

Think It Over

1 Describe the results from above that helped you prepare your hypothesis.

_____

_____

2 State the hypothesis you developed to explain your observations.

_____

_____

3 A California television station warned residents that mudflows are imminent because heavy rains are expected throughout next week. Evaluate the scientific accuracy of the newscaster's claim.

_____

_____

65

MASS MOVEMENT

Weathering and Erosion

The process of erosion moves weathered rock and soil from one place to another. In this activity you will examine how the angle of a slope, such as a hill or mountain, and the presence of water in the soil, affects erosion.

INQUIRY FOCUS *Make Models*

Procedure

Materials

- dry soil, 250-mL cup
- tray, ~20 cm × 35 cm
- water, 150 mL
- 100-mL graduated cylinder
- small plastic bowl, 500-mL
- protractor
- timer
- craft stick

1. Read through the procedure. Then, work with members of your group to determine the quantity of water you will use and the two angles you will test. Write this information in a data table.

2. 🫧 🧍 Put on apron and goggles. Lay the tray out flat in front of you. Place a handful of dry soil near the middle of the tray.

3. Set the timer for 30 seconds. At the same time, start the timer and lift one end of the tray to the first angle your team determined. Use your protractor to help you set the angle.

4. After 30 seconds, record your observations in the data table.

5. Repeat Steps 3 and 4, but lift the same end of the tray to the second angle. Then, return the tray to the horizontal position. Remove the soil and place it in the plastic bowl.

6. Add the amount of water your team determined to the bowl, and use the craft stick to mix the water with the soil. Clean up any spills immediately.

7. Place the wet soil near the middle of the tray.

8. Repeat Steps 3–7. Then dispose of the soil in the designated place. Wash your hands when you are finished.

Think It Over

❶ Compare your results with the results of two other groups. Can you identify any relationship between the amount of water and the amount of soil movement?

_____

_____

❷ From your comparison with other groups, can you identify any relationship between the steepness of the angle and the amount of soil movement?

_____

_____

● **Lab Investigation**

PRE LAB

Sand Hills

Reviewing Content

Gravity is the force that moves objects downhill. It is a major cause of mass movement processes, such as landslides and creep.

Mass movement can happen quickly, as in a landslide that sends rock and soil tumbling downhill in seconds. It can also happen slowly, as in the process of creep that can take many years. The processes of mass movement are more likely to occur on slopes that are steep and unstable, and where sediment is not held firmly in place.

In this lab, you will experiment to find out how the height and width of a hill affect a hill's stability and the probability of mass movement.

Creep

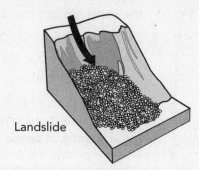

Landslide

Reviewing Inquiry Focus

When you develop a hypothesis, you make a testable statement, in which you state the expected outcome of an experiment based on observation, prior knowledge, or other evidence. In this lab, you will make several sand hills of different heights, and use your observation of their formation and structure to develop a hypothesis on how the height of a sand hill is related to its width. Is there a certain height-to-width ratio that makes a sand hill most stable? As you write your hypothesis, remember that a hypothesis is often a possible explanation for a set of observations.

When you interpret data, you analyze and draw conclusions from data you collect. In this Lab Investigation, you will analyze observations and data. You will use it to draw conclusions about the way the height of a sand hill is related to its width, which will help you develop your hypothesis.

1 How would you collect data on the height and width of a sand hill?

_____

_____

2 In Step 3 of the procedure, you will let sand flow out of a tube and form itself into a sand hill. Why would you let the hill form on its own instead of shaping it yourself?

_____

_____

MASS MOVEMENT

Sand Hills

Problem

What is the relationship between the height and width of a sand hill?

INQUIRY FOCUS
Develop a Hypothesis, Interpret Data, Graph

Materials

dry sand (500 mL) in container

cardboard tube

tray (about 15 cm × 45 cm × 60 cm)

wooden barbecue skewer

masking tape

spoon

metric ruler

pencil or crayon

several sheets of white paper

Procedure

1. Begin by observing how gravity causes mass movement. To start, place the cardboard tube vertically in the center of the tray.

2. 🥽 Put on your goggles. Using the spoon, fill the cardboard tube with dry sand. Take care not to spill the sand around the outside of the tube.

3. Carefully lift the sand-filled tube straight up so that all the sand flows out. As you lift the tube, observe the sand's movement.

4. Develop a hypothesis explaining how you think the height of the sand pile is related to its width for different amounts of sand.

_____

_____

5. Empty the sand in the tray back into its container. Then set up your system for measuring the sand hill. (See the box on the following page that tells you how to measure a sand hill.) Line the tray that will hold the sand hills with white paper, as the procedure in the box instructs.

6. Follow Steps 1–3 and make a new sand hill in the tray lined with white paper.

7. Measure the sand hill's height and width for Test 1 according to the instructions in the box. Record your measurements in the data table below.

Test	1	2	3	4	5
Width					
Height					

MASS MOVEMENT

Name _____ Date_____ Class_____

SAND HILLS *continued*

DIRECTED Inquiry ━━● **Lab Investigation**

8. Now test what happens when you add more sand to the sand hill. Hold your cardboard tube vertically at the peak of the sand hill. Be careful not to push the tube down into the sand hill. Using the spoon, fill the tube with sand as before.

9. Carefully raise the tube and observe the sand's movement.

10. Measure and record the sand hill's height and width for Test 2.

11. Repeat Steps 8–11 at least three more times. After each test, record your results. Be sure to number each test.

12. Wash your hands when you are finished with the lab.

How to Measure a Sand Hill

1. Cover the inside bottom of the tray with unlined white paper and tape it firmly in place.

2. Mark off points 0.5 cm apart along one side of the paper in the tray.

3. Carefully draw the sand hill's outline on the paper. The line should go completely around the base of the hill.

4. Now measure the width of the hill, using the marks you made along the edge of the paper. The width will be the diameter of the circle of the hill's outline that you drew.

5. Measure the sand hill's height by inserting a barbecue skewer through its center. Make a mark on the skewer at the top of the hill. Try not to disturb the sand.

6. Remove the skewer and use the ruler to measure how much of the skewer was buried in the hill.

MASS MOVEMENT

Analyze and Conclude

1 **Graph** Make a graph showing how the sand hill's height and width changed with each test. *Hint: Use the x-axis of the graph for width; use the y-axis for height.*

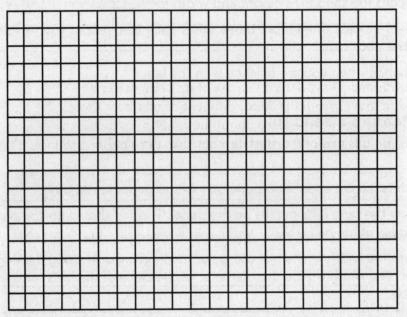

2 **Interpret Data** What does your graph show about the relationship between a hill's height and width?

_____

_____

3 **Draw Conclusions** Does your graph support your hypothesis about the sand hill's height and width? Why or why not?

_____

_____

_____

4 **Develop a Hypothesis** How would you revise your original hypothesis after examining your data? Give reasons for your answer.

_____

_____

_____

DIRECTED Inquiry → ● **Lab Investigation**

POST LAB

Sand Hills

① **Predict** Predict what would happen if you continued the experiment for five more tests. Extend your graph on the previous page with a dashed line to show your prediction. How could you test your prediction?

_____

_____

② **Design an Experiment** Do you think the use of different materials, such as wet sand or gravel, would produce different results from those using dry sand? Make a new hypothesis about the relationship between height and width in hills made of materials other than dry sand.

_____

_____

③ **Draw Conclusions** Based on the data collected in this lab, describe a sand hill with a stable form.

_____

_____

④ **Infer** How do the results of this lab explain the likelihood of mass movement, such as a landslide, on a hill?

_____

_____

⑤ **Summarize** Describe what you have learned in this lab about the relationship between the height and width of a sand hill.

What I learned

_____

What I still want to know

_____

Communicate

Write a paragraph in which you discuss how you measured your sand hill. Did any problems you had in making your measurements affect your results? How did you adjust your measurement technique to solve these problems?

MASS MOVEMENT

OPEN Inquiry   40 min

Sand Hills
Problem

What is the relationship between the height and width of a sand hill?

Materials

500 mL of dry sand

cardboard tube

tray (about 15 cm
  × 45 cm × 60 cm)

wooden barbecue
  skewer

masking tape

spoon

metric ruler

pencil or crayon

several sheets of
  white paper

safety goggles

Design an Experiment

1. In this activity, you will explore the relationship between the heights and widths of sand hills.

   - First, you will practice making sand hills. Take the tray provided by your teacher and use the paper to cover its interior surface.

   - Next, stand the cardboard tube upright, on one end, in the middle of the tray. Use the spoon to fill the tube with sand.

   - When the tube is nearly full, slowly and steadily pull the tube straight up so that the sand falls out of the bottom and forms a cone-shaped hill.

   - Is the hill's height greater than, less than, or approximately equal to the hill's width?

     _____

     _____

2. Now you will design an experiment to test a hypothesis about the height-to-width relationship in sand hills. Develop your hypothesis and write it here.

   _____

   _____

3. Look at the rest of the materials provided by your teacher. They can be used to measure the width and height of sand hills. Figure out how you will use them for this purpose, and practice with a new sand hill. Determine how many trials you will run to test your hypothesis.

4. In the spaces below, outline your procedure and draw a table for recording your results.

5. 🔖 ⚠ Tell your teacher what your hypothesis is and how you will test it. Once approved, run your experiment, record your results in the table. Graph your results in the grid provided below.

Procedure

_____
_____
_____
_____

Data Table

Graph

MASS MOVEMENT

OPEN Inquiry •——— Lab Investigation

Analyze and Conclude

1 **Develop a Hypothesis** Describe the results of your experiment in general terms and what they reveal about your hypothesis.

_____

_____

_____

_____

2 **Interpret Data** Describe any patterns you noticed in your data.

_____

_____

_____

_____

3 **Infer** What are the forces acting upon the sand and the sand hill, causing the hill to take its shape?

_____

_____

_____

_____

4 **Design an Experiment** How would you run this experiment a second time if you had the same materials but also water to work with? How would your hypothesis change, if at all?

_____

_____

_____

_____

POST LAB

Sand Hills

1 **Design an Experiment** Describe any problems you had with this activity, and how you might avoid them if you could redo or redesign the experiment.

_____

_____

2 **Predict** How would rain, wind, and other weather phenomena influence the shape of sand hills?

_____

_____

3 **Infer** Imagine you are a highway trooper. You hear of two overturned trucks on opposite sides of the highway. One tipped over with a truckload of dry sand. The other tipped over with the same volume of rocks. Which truck accident is most likely to disrupt traffic in the other lanes? Explain.

_____

_____

4 **Summarize** Describe what you have learned in this lab about the relationship between the height and width of a sand hill?

What I learned _____

_____

What I still want to know _____

_____

Communicate

Imagine that you are a builder hired by a family that wants to build a home at the top of a hill. They have three potential hilltop sites, and they want your help in deciding which site will be safest in the long run, in terms of erosion and landslides. Put together a presentation for the family that explains the force and variables involved in landslides and erosion. Be sure to touch upon:

- the different behaviors of hillsides made of different materials
- the effects of outside factors such as weather
- the probability that building on any kind of hillside is probably not very safe

━━━━━━━━━━━━━━━━━━ Inquiry Warm-Up ━━━━━━━━━━━━● 15 min ⏰

How Does Moving Water Wear Away Rocks?

Moving water is a major agent of erosion. In this activity, you will use water dripping from a faucet and a bar of soap to model erosion by water.

INQUIRY FOCUS Predict

Procedure

1. Obtain two bars of soap that are the same size and brand.

2. 🥽 🦺 Open a faucet just enough to let the water drip out very slowly. Put on an apron and goggles.

3. Place one bar of soap in a dry place. Place the other bar of soap under the faucet. Predict the effect of the dripping water droplets on the soap.

4. Let the faucet drip for 10 minutes.

5. Turn off the faucet and observe both bars of soap.

6. 🧼 Return the soap to the designated place. Wash your hands when you are finished.

Materials

2 bars of soap
cold water faucet
watch or clock with second hand

Think It Over

1 What did you predict would be the effect of the water dripping onto the soap?

_____

_____

2 What would the bar of soap under the dripping faucet look like if you left it in place for another 10 minutes? For another hour? How could you speed up the process or slow it down?

_____

_____

_____

3 How does this activity model erosion on Earth's surface?

_____

_____

Quick Lab

15 min

Raindrops Falling

When raindrops fall, they cause erosion of soil, which moves over Earth's surface in runoff and eventually enters streams and rivers. In this activity, you will investigate the way the force of falling raindrops affects soil.

INQUIRY FOCUS Draw Conclusions

Procedure

1. Put on apron and goggles. Fill a petri dish with fine-textured soil to a depth of about 1 cm. Make sure the soil has a smooth, flat surface, but do not pack it firmly in the dish.

2. Place the dish in the center of the newspaper.

3. Fill the dropper full of water. Squeeze a large drop of water from a height of 1 m onto the surface of the soil. Repeat this four times.

4. Use the meter stick to measure the distance the soil splashed from the dish. Record your observations in the data table below.

5. Repeat Steps 1–4, this time from a height of 2 m.

6. Clean up your lab station. Wash your hands when you are finished.

Materials

petri dish
fine-textured soil
newspaper
plastic dropper
water
meter stick

1-Meter Drop		2-Meter Drop	
Trial	Splash Distance	Trial	Splash Distance
1		1	
2		2	
3		3	
4		4	

Think It Over

1 Draw conclusions about which distance produced the greater amount of erosion. Why was this the case?

_____

2 Based on the results of this lab, infer what type of rainfall causes the most erosion. Explain.

_____

WATER EROSION

⏰ **Quick Lab** 15 min

Erosion Cube

Water erosion forms a variety of landforms, such as waterfalls and caves with spectacular formations. In this activity, you will use water and a block of sugar cubes to observe the effects of water erosion on underground rock.

INQUIRY FOCUS Observe

Procedure

1. 🧤 🥽 Put on apron and goggles. In a small dish, build a block out of 27 small sugar cubes. Your block should be 3 sugar cubes on a side. **CAUTION:** *Do not taste or eat any of the sugar cubes.*

2. Fold a paper towel so that it covers the top of the block of cubes.

3. Wet the paper towel and place it on the block of cubes. Let it stand for about 15 minutes. Every few minutes use a dropper to place a few drops of water on the paper towel to keep it wet.

4. Remove the paper towel and observe the effect on the block of cubes.

Materials

small dish
27 small sugar cubes
paper towel
water
dropper

Think It Over

1 What happened to your block of cubes?

_____

_____

2 How is the effect of water on the block of cubes similar to that of groundwater on limestone?

_____

_____

_____

Inquiry Warm-Up ● 10 min ⏰

How Do Glaciers Change the Land?

A glacier is a large mass of ice that moves slowly over the land. As they move, glaciers slowly change the land beneath them. In this activity, you will model a glacier moving across Earth's surface.

INQUIRY FOCUS Infer

Procedure

1. 🧤 🥽 Put on apron and goggles. Put some sand in a small plastic cup.

2. Add enough water to cover the sand in the cup, and freeze it overnight.

3. Remove the block of ice from the cup. Hold the ice with a paper towel.

4. Rub the ice, sand side down, over a bar of soap. Observe what happens to the surface of the soap.

Materials

sand
plastic cup
water
freezer
paper towel
bar of soap

Think It Over

1 Based on your observations, infer how this activity demonstrates abrasion.

_____

_____

_____

2 How does the ice cube model the way a glacier changes Earth's surface?

_____

_____

_____

_____

Quick Lab

5 min

Surging Glaciers

Glaciers usually move no more than a few meters a day. But sometimes they move in quick bursts called surges. In this activity, you will observe conditions that could cause a glacier to surge.

INQUIRY FOCUS Observe

Procedure

1. Push the plastic lid across the floor when the floor is dry.

2. ⚠ Place some water on the floor. Then push the plastic lid across the floor again. **CAUTION: _The floor around you might be slippery._**

3. Dry the floor with some paper towels.

Materials

hard surface floor
plastic lid
water
paper towels

Think It Over

1 What did you observe when the floor was dry? What did you observe when it was wet? How would you explain the difference?

_____

_____

_____

2 How does this model conditions that can cause glaciers to surge?

_____

_____

_____

Name _____ Date_____ Class_____

Modeling Valleys

The shape of a valley can tell you whether it was formed by moving water or moving ice. In this activity, you will model the formation of valleys both by moving water and by moving ice, then contrast the resulting landforms.

INQUIRY FOCUS Make a Model

Procedure

1. 🧤 👓 Put on apron and goggles. Set up a stream table with a layer of soil about 10 cm thick. Turn on a steady trickle of water. Turn off the water after about five minutes.

2. Examine the valley that formed in the soil. Sketch your observations below.

3. Place an ice cube at the top of the stream-formed valley. Slowly push the ice cube down the valley. Again, examine the valley and sketch your observations below.

4. 🧼 Wash your hands when you finish the lab.

Materials

stream table (with hose attached)
soil
water
ice

Valley Formed by Moving Water	Valley Formed by Moving Ice

Think It Over

1 Based on your observations, what shape do valleys formed by streams have? What shape do valleys formed by glaciers have?

_____

_____

2 How could the data you gathered in this lab help geologists determine the geological history of an area?

_____

_____

GLACIAL EROSION

15 min

What Is Sand Made Of?

Ocean waves often slam onto beaches made of sand. Where does the sand come from? In this activity, you will examine two different samples of beach sand and pose questions about the origins of sand.

INQUIRY FOCUS Pose Questions

Procedure

1. 🥽 Put on your goggles. Pour a spoonful of sand from one of the labeled containers into the tray.

2. Examine this sample of beach sand with a hand lens.

3. Use the data table below to record properties of the sand grains, such as color and shape. Observe whether the grains are smooth and rounded or angular and rough. Return the sample of sand to the container.

4. Examine a second sample. Repeat Step 3 to compare the two samples.

5. 🧼 Return the sand samples to the designated area. Wash your hands with soap and warm water when you are finished.

Materials

sand from 2 beaches
hand lens
plastic spoon
small tray

	Color characteristics	Shape characteristics
Sample 1		
Sample 2		

Think It Over

1 What questions do you need to answer to understand beach sand? Use what you know about erosion and deposition to help you think of questions.

_____

_____

_____

2 How do the two different samples of sand differ?

_____

_____

_____

WAVE EROSION

_____ **Quick Lab** ●————— 15 min

Shaping a Coastline

Waves shape a coastline through erosion and deposition. In this activity, you will examine how the direction and strength of waves shape a coastline.

INQUIRY FOCUS Control Variables

Procedure

1. 🧤 🥼 Put on apron and goggles. Place a pencil under one end of the pan so it rests on the table at a slight angle.

2. Pour sand into the higher end of the pan, building it up to model a beach.

3. Add a few rocks to your beach.

4. Pour water into the lower end of the pan.

5. Hold the ruler in the water, parallel to the beach. Push the ruler lengthwise through the water toward the beach to create a series of small waves. Observe what happens as the waves hit the beach directly.

6. Change the direction of the water hitting the beach by moving the ruler through the water at an angle toward the beach.

7. Observe the effects on the shape of the coastline.

8. 🧽 Clean up your set-up as directed by your teacher. Wash your hands when you are finished.

Materials

shallow metal pan,
~22 cm × 33 cm
× 5 cm
sand, 250 mL
water
small rocks
plastic ruler, 15 cm
pencil

Think It Over

1 How did the shape of the beach change when waves hit it directly? When they hit at an angle?

_____

_____

2 Did the beach erode differently where the rocks were located? Explain.

_____

_____

3 List two additional variables that you could test that might affect shoreline erosion.

_____

WAVE EROSION

━━━━━━━━━━━━━━━━ **Inquiry Warm-Up** ━━━━━━━━━━━● 🕐 **10 min**

How Does Moving Air Affect Sediment?

Moving air, or wind, sweeps over Earth's surface and changes the land. In this activity, you will model moving air to observe how it causes erosion.

INQUIRY FOCUS Observe

Procedure

1. 🥽 Put on your goggles. Cover the bottom of the pan with a flat layer of cornmeal 1–2 cm deep.

2. Use the straw to gently blow over the layer of cornmeal. Observe what happens. **CAUTION: *Do not blow the cornmeal in the direction of another student.***

Materials

aluminum pan
cornmeal
straw
metric ruler

Think It Over

1 How did the air you blew through the straw affect the flat layer of cornmeal?

_____

_____

_____

2 How does this activity model the interaction of wind and sediment on Earth's surface?

_____

_____

_____

WIND EROSION

Quick Lab

10 min

Desert Pavement

Deflation is the process in which wind removes surface sediment. Some landforms, such as desert pavement, are largely the result of deflation. In this activity, you will model the formation of desert pavement.

INQUIRY FOCUS Make a Model

Procedure

1. Put on apron and goggles. Place a few coins into the bottom of the pan.

2. ⚠ Sprinkle enough flour over the coins to cover them. **CAUTION: *You should not do this lab if you have a grain allergy.***

3. Bend the straw and position it about 2 cm above the pan with the short end facing up. Blow air gently through the short end of the straw across the top of the flour for 3–5 seconds. **CAUTION: *Do not draw in any flour through the straw. Do not blow the flour toward anyone.***

4. Clean up your lab set-up as designated by your teacher. Wash your hands when you are finished.

Materials

several coins
aluminum pan
flour
elbow straw
metric ruler

Think It Over

1. What did you observe when you blew a stream of air over the flour?

_____

_____

2. Predict what would happen if you blew over the flour for a longer time.

_____

_____

3. How does your experiment model the formation of desert pavement? What do the coins represent? What does the flour represent?

_____

_____

_____

WIND EROSION

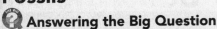
Fossils

Answering the Big Question

The activities in this lesson will help students answer the Big Question by having them observe fossils in a rock, model different modes of fossil formation, and model a part of the fossil record.

Inquiry Warm-Up

What's in a Rock?

Inquiry Focus

Infer—suggesting a possible explanation as to how fossils become parts of rocks by observing the texture of a fossiliferous rock

Group Size Individuals

Class Time 10 minutes

Advance Preparation (30 minutes)

Obtain fossil-bearing rocks from the geology department of a local college or university or from a scientific supply company.

Procedure Tips

1. Ask students to complete their observations and drawings before discussing their rocks with others.
2. If time allows, have pairs of students exchange rocks and repeat the activity with the new rock.

Answers

1. Most students will know that the preserved remains and imprints in the rocks are evidence of once-living things (fossils).
2. Sample Answer: An organism died and became trapped in sediment. As the sediment got compacted and cemented, the remains became embedded in the rock.

Quick Lab

Sweet Fossils

Unlocking the Key Concept

This activity will help students recognize that fossils of soft parts form when dead organisms are protected from factors that can cause decay.

Inquiry Focus

Observe—using the senses to gather information about how fossils of soft parts of organisms form

Group Size Individuals or pairs

Class Time 15 minutes

Safety

Remind students that, unless they are directed to by their teacher, they should never eat anything used in the science classroom, including the sugar used in this activity.

Advance Preparation (10 minutes)

Purchase enough sugar cubes so that each student or pair of students has three cubes.

Procedure Tips

Using warm water will help the sugar dissolve faster.

Answers

1. The sugar cube completely enclosed in the clay did not dissolve at all. The cube partially enclosed in clay completely dissolved.
2. The clay prevented the completely enclosed sugar cube from reacting with the water. It protected the sugar from the surrounding environment.
3. Fossils of soft parts of organisms form when sediment completely covers organic remains. This prevents them from decay or being eaten.

Quick Lab

Modeling Trace Fossils

Unlocking the Key Concept

This activity will help students recognize that not all fossils are preserved remains. Trace fossils are evidence of the behavior or activity of ancient organisms.

Inquiry Focus

Infer—suggesting a possible explanation or drawing a conclusion about the behavior of an ancient organism by observing model trace fossils

Group Size Groups

Class Time 15 minutes

A TRIP THROUGH GEOLOGIC TIME

Advance Preparation (20 minutes)

1. Gather objects that groups might use to produce their trace fossils—paper clips, coins, shells, keys, straws, toothpicks, or fine-toothed combs. Students can use small, plastic animals to make fossil footprints, but these should be used discreetly so that other teams do not see the animals that left the prints.

2. Provide rolling pins or other cylindrical implements to help flatten the clay.

Procedure Tips

1. Students can produce footprints with the small plastic animals or by using the edge of any of the suggested objects to carve a pair of footprints into the clay. For example, a toothpick could be used to carve a pair of bird footprints into the clay.

2. Before they make any fossils, have student teams spend 3–4 minutes discussing what they will be doing. For example, footprints are trace fossils that can indicate both movement and the size of the organism that made them. A pair of prints that are relatively close together suggest that the organism was walking very slowly. A pair of prints that are far apart could indicate that the animal was running or had a relatively large stride.

3. Fossilized nests are trace fossils that indicate the size of the eggs laid by an organism as well as how a certain organism may have cared for its young.

4. Burrows are trace fossils that can indicate that the organism that made them lived at least part of its life underground, or they can represent a search for food. Fossil burrows can be made by coring the clay with a straw.

5. At the conclusion of the activity, select some of the trace fossils and discuss them with the class. Focus on how scientists would use this information to build their understanding of how ancient animals might have lived or how they might have moved.

6. Sample Answer to Procedure Step 3:

Describe trace fossil observation	Describe your inference
Small thin footprints that resemble a capital W	Could have been made by an ancient bird
Small tunnel-shaped impression in the clay	Could have been made by an ancient worm or other burrowing animal
Widely separated, large footprints with three toes or parts	Could have been made by a dinosaur or mammal
Long, narrow, winding imprint	Could have been made by an ancient snake or a dinosaur's tail dragging on the ground
Small bowl-like impression	Could be the remnants of a fossilized nest made by an animal that laid eggs and kept them in nests

Answers

1. Students' answers will depend on the trace fossils observed and the imagination of the students. Refer to the table above for specific examples of possible trace fossils.

2. Answers will vary based on the trace fossils produced by students. Refer to the table for possible inferences that could be made based on students' observations of the model fossils.

Quick Lab

Modeling the Fossil Record

Unlocking the Key Concept

This activity will help students infer that fossils provide information about ancient organisms and how they might have changed over time, as well as clues to past environments.

Inquiry Focus

Infer—suggesting possible explanations for observed changes in fossils and suggestions about where and how the living organisms might have lived

Group Size Individuals or pairs

Class Time 20 minutes

Safety
Remind students to take care when using the scissors.

Advance Preparation (20 minutes)
Have reference books available and/or provide students with several appropriate websites that discuss the evolution of horses, elephants, sharks, or horseshoe crabs.

Answers
1. Look for answers that include observations that, except for the horseshoe crab, their organism became larger and more complex over time. The horseshoe crab has changed little, if at all, since it appeared on Earth.
2. In a series of rock layers that has not been disturbed by Earth processes, the oldest rocks are always at the bottom of the section and the youngest rocks are always at the top of the section. Each new layer is deposited on top of the previously deposited layer.
3. Sample Answer: The horse and elephant are terrestrial organisms, while the shark and horseshoe crab are marine. Students might elaborate more if the information is available.

The Relative Age Of Rocks
Answering the Big Question
The activities in this lesson will help students answer the Big Question by having them interpret rock sequences to determine what the sequences tell us about Earth's past.

Inquiry Warm-Up
Which Layer Is the Oldest?
Inquiry Focus
Observe—using the senses to gather information about model rock sequences

Group Size Individuals or pairs

Class Time 15 minutes

Safety
Remind students to be careful when using the plastic knife.

Advance Preparation (15 minutes)
Obtain enough clay so that each student or pair of students has a small orange-sized ball of each color.

Procedure Tips
1. Before students begin to cut their models, remind them not to cut all the way through to the bowl. Have them leave one layer covering the bowl.
2. If you want to use the clay again, give students sheets of wax paper and tell them to place a sheet between each layer of clay.

Answers
1. The rock layer at the bottom of the undeformed sequence is the oldest.
2. In the dome structure, the oldest layer of rock appears at the center of the structure (even if it is higher than the other layers).
3. The oldest layer would appear along the outer edges of the depression.

Lab Investigation
Exploring Geologic Time Through Core Samples
Unlocking the Key Concept
Both Versions This activity will help students understand how scientists use cores of subsurface rocks to help interpret Earth's history.

Answers—Pre Lab
Both Versions:
1. Students will be observing different types of rock layers and "fossils" and their relative ages.
2. Students will be using relative dating methods to interpret their cores.

Answers—Do the Math
The deepest hole penetrating Earth's crust was drilled nearly 50 years ago by scientists at the Kola Institute in the former Soviet Union. The drilling rig also took various core samples of the rocks encountered.
12,262 km/24 y = ~511 km/y;
511 km/75 km/h = 6.8 h

Inquiry Focus

Both Versions:

Observe—using the senses to gather and record information about a model core sample

Make Models—using household materials to model Earth's rock layers and the use of core samples to examine those layers

Measure—quantifying the thicknesses of model rock layers

Group Size

Directed Inquiry Groups

Open Inquiry Pairs

Preparation Time

Both Versions 45 minutes

Class Time

Both Versions 40 minutes
Safety

1. Have a broom or brush and a dust pan and rags or paper towels available to sweep and wipe up any spills.
2. Students should wear aprons and gloves during the activity. They should wash their hands when finished.

Advance Preparation (45 minutes)

Both Versions

1. Ask students to bring in empty, clean 1-L gable top milk or juice cartons. Cut off the tops of the cartons to create rectangular containers that are open at the top.
2. Obtain the straws, rods, colored sand, potting soil, and seeds and grains. You might ask students to supply some of these materials as well. Note that the sediment (sand and soil) and "fossils" must be small enough to fit in the straws. The rods must be small enough to fit into the straws. The straws should have a large diameter, be sturdy, and not have a flexible section. Finally, the "fossils" should be such that they will not dissolve or break down in the damp sediment.

Alternative Materials

Any tall, narrow containers, such as potato chip cans, can be used in place of the milk cartons. Note, however, that the containers must be opaque so that students obtain information about the layers only from their cores. Small plastic or glass beads can be used as fossils. Clear, hard plastic tubing, cut to size, from a building supply store can be used in place of the straws.

Procedure Tips

Directed Inquiry:

1. Have students review the definition of *index fossil* before they construct their models.
2. To simplify this lab, you might want to have each group use only one index fossil.
3. Suggest that students lightly pack the different layers of sediment so that they remain consolidated when the core is removed from the straw.
4. Remind students to make their cores perpendicular to the bottom of the container.

Open Inquiry:

1. Explain to the groups that they will be preparing models of rock layers for each other. After a group has used core sampling to examine the rock layers made by another group, their findings will be compared to that other group's rock layer "blueprint."
2. Discuss relative aging and superposition. Ask, **What is the law of superposition and how does it relate to relative aging?** (*The law of superposition states that in horizontal layers of sedimentary rock, the oldest layer is at the bottom and younger layers are nearer the top. Therefore, rock and fossils found below a layer are relatively older than those in the layer above.*) Ask, **What is an index fossil and how does it help with determining the age of rock layers and other fossils?** (*An index fossil is from an organism that was widely distributed but lived within a fairly narrow period of geologic time. Its presence in, below, or above other layers with other fossils can tell scientists how old those other layers and fossils are.*)
3. Look over the rock layer model blueprints of each group, including their planned distribution of fossils, before they build the models and pass them on to another group for core sampling. Use random assignments for the swaps of models among the groups, and make sure the students understand which end of the coring straw corresponds to the oldest rock layers.

4. Help students determine the right amount of water to add to each layer. Too little water and the core sample will not stick inside the straw; too much water and the soil will be too "soupy."

Answers—Analyze and Conclude
Directed Inquiry:

1. The "rock" at the bottom of the core is the oldest because it "formed" first. The "rock" at the top of the core is the youngest because it "formed" last.

2. The model is similar to actual rock layers because it is made of different layers of sediment that are stacked together. The model is different in that the sediment is not rock and was made by people. The layers were made in a short time span rather than over long periods of time.

3. Look for answers that discuss the presence of an abundance of one type of fossil in only one or two layers. Students won't be able to address the widespread nature of the fossil, but they can note their abundance and occurrence over a short period of time.

4. Sample Answer: Fossils show that different types of organisms lived at different points in geologic time. Fossils also show that life forms change over time.

5. Look for answers to include that folding and events that produce unconformities can change the order of rocks in an area. Geologists can use fossils to determine the relative ages of disturbed rocks if they know the relative ages of the fossils.

Open Inquiry:

1. Sample Answer: There were four layers. The oldest was dark and moist, like soil; the next up was red sand; the second youngest was a very thin layer of white sand, and; the youngest was like dried leaves. The presence of sesame seeds in the thin white layer suggests that it was the index fossil.

2. Sample Answer: The sesame seeds were only present in the one layer, and that layer was distinct and fairly narrow in depth.

3. Sample Answer: We missed a few of the fossils that had been put in a couple of the layers.

4. Look for answers indicating that taking more core samples would have produced more data and given a more complete picture of what the rock layers looked like and what fossils they contained.

Answers—Post Lab
Directed Inquiry:

1. Tilting the straw would have produced an inaccurate core of the model rock layers. The layers would have been thicker than they actually are.

2. Sample Answer: The relative ages and the thicknesses of subsurface rocks can be determined by observing the core. The presence and type of fossils can also be determined.

3. Look for answers that include at least one specific statement about what the student learned, such as how subsurface rocks are studied or how relative ages of rocks are determined. Answers about what students still want to know should relate to relative dating methods or coring rocks beneath the surface.

Communicate—Students should note some similarities between their observations and the original sections. Slight differences might be the result of shifting of sediment layers either during coring or as the cores were removed from the straws. Differences might also be the result of inserting the straws at an angle rather than perpendicular to the bottom of the container. Finally, the presence or absence of different fossils might not be observed if the fossils are very small.

Open Inquiry:

1. Sample Answer: More core samples should be taken, and a stronger corer would be easier to use. Some of the sediments tended to crumble too easily.

2. Look for answers indicating an understanding that a real-world core sample might not contain as many fossils, and the rock layers would take much longer to cut into and remove from the ground. Folds, intrusions, and other things could disrupt the sequence of the layers.

3. Sample Answer: You could use a core sample to determine the location and density of the best bedrock for building upon, and index fossils might also aid in this.

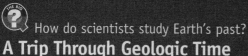
4. Look for answers that include that the view of the exposed layers in the canyon is a lot like looking at the sides of a core sample. You can measure the relative thicknesses and depths of the layers, and you might be able to see fossils as well.

Communicate—Look for answers that show that students understand the concept of superposition and know what an index fossil is. Students should be able to describe core sampling and how it can be used for relative dating. Student videos should include graphics or charts and illustrations.

Quick Lab

How Did It Form?

🔑 Unlocking the Key Concept

This activity will help students model how forces can change rocks, sometimes making it more difficult to determine the relative age of a rock bed.

Inquiry Focus

Make Models—creating physical representations of rock sequences and simulating Earth processes that can change the rock layers in the sequences

Group Size Groups

Class Time 20 minutes

Safety

Remind students to use care when using the knife.

Advance Preparation (10 minutes)

Provide each group with enough modeling clay to make the rock sequence described in Step 1. If you wish to reuse the clay, also provide each group with waxed paper and instruct students to place a sheet of the paper between layers of clay.

Procedure Tips

1. Stress that to accurately simulate the processes involved in creating the rock sequence, the models must be constructed from the bottom up.
2. When modeling the left sequence, students can reuse colors of clay for the rocks deposited on top of the unconformity.

Answers

1. Sample Answer: Each rock layer was deposited. The [darkest brown] layer was deposited first and is the oldest. The [orange] layer was deposited last and is the youngest. Over time, the top three layers were eroded. More time passed and three more rock layers were deposited and an unconformity formed.
2. Sample Answer: Each rock layer was deposited. The [darkest brown] layer was deposited first and is the oldest. The [orange] layer was deposited last and is the youngest. Forces pushed on the rocks and caused them to fold. Folding caused some of the older layers to be positioned above the younger layers and vice versa.

Radioactive Dating

❓ Answering the Big Question

The activities in this lesson will help students answer the Big Question by having them model radioactive decay and date objects by modeling radioactive methods.

Inquiry Warm-Up

How Long Till It's Gone?

Inquiry Focus

Predict—making an educated guess about how much of a clay cube will remain after it has been halved several times

Group Size Individuals

Class Time 10 minutes

Safety

Remind students to take care when using the knife, especially as the cube gets smaller.

Procedure Tips

1. Inform students that exact measurements are not necessary and they should simply estimate when cutting each piece in "half."
2. Sample Prediction for Procedure Step 3: There will be one eighth of the original cube left after two more cuts.

Answers

1. By cutting the original cube three times, the cube is reduced to one eighth its original size.

2. The remaining cube will be very small, possibly too small to cut in half again. If it were possible, though, the piece would be $\frac{1}{64}$ the original size after three more cuts.

3. Even though the cube is now larger, the remaining piece would again be one eighth its original size after three cuts.

Quick Lab

The Dating Game

🔑 Unlocking the Key Concept

This activity will help students better understand the process of radioactive decay.

Inquiry Focus

Graph—organizing data in a visual way, such as in a bar graph, to show the relationship between radioactive decay and time

Group Size Pairs

Class Time 20 minutes

Advance Preparation (10 minutes)

Ask each pair of students to contribute 100 pennies (2 rolls) for their models.

Alternative Materials

Two-centimeter squares or circles of construction paper with *H* written on one side and *T* written on the other side can be substituted for pennies. You will need 100 squares or circles for each student pair. If you choose to use the paper models instead of coins, cut them ahead of time using scissors or a large paper punch.

Sample Data

1. See the sample data table below.

Trial	Pennies Heads Up	Pennies Tails Up
1	52	48
2	25	27
3	13	12
4	6	7

2. Students' graphs should be very similar to the sample bar graph below.

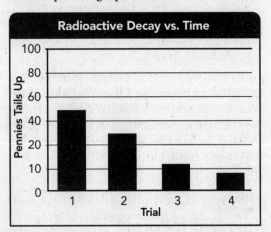

Radioactive Decay vs. Time

Answers

1. Half-life is the time it takes for half of the number of radioactive atoms to decay. Decay here is represented by the heads side of the pennies. During each trial, approximately 50% of the pennies will land on tails, representing the parent material, and 50% of the pennies will land on heads, representing the daughter material that has formed after each half-life.

2. Students should calculate a model half-life by taking the total time spent dumping the pennies and dividing this time by the number of trials—4.

Quick Lab

How Old Is It?

🔑 Unlocking the Key Concept

This activity will help students understand how radiometric ages of certain rocks and fossils can be determined.

Inquiry Focus

Calculate—using mathematical processes to calculate the ages of various rocks and fossils

Group Size Pairs

Class Time 10 minutes

Advance Preparation (20 minutes)

Use the data in the table below, colored pencils, and large, unruled index cards to make two complete sets of mini-reports to distribute to students. Each card, or mini-report, should include a simple drawing of the rock or fossil on one side of the card, and a brief description of the rock or fossil, the number of half-lives that have passed since the rock or fossil formed, and the name of the radioactive element that was used to date the rock or fossil on the other side of the card. See the sample data table below.

Procedure Tips

1. Remind students what they learned about parent and daughter products in the previous lab, and that it is the ratio of these atoms that determines the number of half lives that have passed.

2. If necessary, write out the numbers one million and one billion to help students with their calculations.

3. If students seem confused or surprised that the number of half-lives that have passed is not a whole number, remind them that at 6 months from their birth dates, they are 12.5 or 13.5 years old.

4. Display the age results of all the teams on the board or the overhead projector. Have volunteers redo the math if there are conflicting ages for the same rock or fossil.

Answers

1. The rock from Minnesota is the oldest object; the cloth from the mummy is the youngest.

2. The two samples of charcoal, the wood, and the mummy wrappings were all dated with carbon-14. Carbon-14 is used to date once-living things because C-14 is part of living organisms. Once an organism dies, the C-14 in its body gradually decreases as it decays.

The Geologic Time Scale

Answering the Big Question

The activities in this lesson will help students answer the Big Question by having them make timelines to organize events in their lives and Earth's long past.

Inquiry Warm-Up

This Is Your Life!

Inquiry Focus

Make Models—creating a scaled, physical representation of important events in students' lives

Group Size Individuals

Class Time 15 minutes

Data Table—How Old Is It?

Description of the fossil or the rock sample	Number of half-lives that have passed	Radioactive element used to date the rock/fossil	Approximate age (years)
Cloth from a mummy	0.358	C-14	2051
Charcoal from a tree that burned in a volcanic eruption	1.158	C-14	6,640
Charcoal from an old rock shelter	1.768	C-14	10,130
Wood frozen in a glacier	2.031	C-14	11,638
Volcanic rock in California	0.999	U-235	700 million
Pikes Peak granite	0.023	U-238	1.03 billion
Gneiss from Finland	0.193	Th-232	2.7 billion
Gneiss from Minnesota	0.074	Rb-87	3.6 billion

Procedure Tips

Students need not list very personal events. Suggest that they list their birth dates, graduations, important birthdays, or "firsts"—when they got their first bikes, the first time they moved to a new house/apartment, and so on.

Answers

1. If students follow the suggested divisions, the most important events of their lives will probably fall within the middle school years.

2. Most students will probably remember more recent events in their lives than events that took place earlier in their lives.

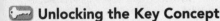

Going Back in Time

🔑 Unlocking the Key Concept

This activity will help students get a better understanding of the immenseness of geologic time by comparing the major units of the geologic time scale to distances in a long hallway.

Inquiry Focus

Make Models—creating a physical representation of the enormous span of geologic time

Group Size Class

Class Time 25 minutes

Alternative Materials

This activity can also be done on an athletic field that measures 100 meters.

Procedure Tips

1. If time allows, show students how you calculated the distances, or have them calculate a few on their own.

2. Give students the values that correspond to their eras or periods and have them accurately measure the distances from the start of the Precambrian (0 yd/0 m). The points at which to place the poster boards are given below.
   Start of Paleozoic: 87.93 m
   Start of Ordovician: 88.89 m
   Start of Silurian: 90.22 m
   Start of Devonian: 90.91 m
   Start of Carboniferous: 92.13 m
   Start of Permian: 93.56 m
   Start of Triassic: 94.56 m

Start of Jurassic: 95.42 m
Start of Cretaceous: 96.80 m
Start of Paleogene: 99.06 m
Start of Neogene: 99.53 m
Start of Quaternary: 99.96 m

3. If time allows, ask students additional questions about the geologic time scale as plotted in the hallway.

4. If you want to reuse the poster boards, assign a student to collect the signs when the activity is completed.

Answers

1. 87.93 m

2. The geologic time scale divisions are based on the presence of fossils. Precambrian time represents that very long part of Earth history in which most organisms were small, with no hard body parts, so they left behind few fossils.

3. The Paleozoic Era lasted longer than the Mesozoic Era. The Paleozoic Era was 6.63 m long and the Mesozoic Era was 4.50 m long.

Early Earth

❓ Answering the Big Question

The activities in this lesson will help students answer the Big Question by having them model how Earth may have formed and by having them study representative fossils from Precambrian time.

Inquiry Warm-Up

How Could Planet Earth Form in Space?

Inquiry Focus

Make Models—creating a physical representation of how Earth may have formed

Group Size Individuals

Class Time 10 minutes

Safety

1. Insist that students wear their safety goggles for the entire activity to prevent iron filings from getting into their eyes.

2. Make sure students wash their hands once they have completed the activity.

Advance Preparation (10 minutes)

Obtain the iron filings and circular magnets from a scientific supply company. Flat circular magnets will work best for this activity as the paper will lie flatter and closer to the desktop.

Procedure Tips

1. Caution students to blow gently through the straw so as not to spread the iron filings all over the paper or their work areas.

2. Be sure that students do not blow the iron filings in the direction of other students.

3. Sample Answer to Procedure Step 5: Students' drawings should show the iron filings clustered on top of the magnet, in a semi-spherical shape.

Answers

1. The model Earth would grow in size as the iron filings continued to accumulate on top of the magnet.

2. The activity simulates how materials in space may have come together to form Earth as the result of the force of gravity. In this model, the force of gravity is represented by the attraction of the iron filings to the poles of the magnet. The activity differs from Earth's actual formation in that the materials that made Earth accumulated from all directions in space, not just from one direction.

Quick Lab

Learning from Fossils

🔑 Unlocking the Key Concept

This activity will help students get a better understanding of how stromatolites grew.

Inquiry Focus

Infer—suggesting a possible explanation about the bacteria that form stromatolites

Group Size Groups of 5 students

Class Time 20 minutes

Advance Preparation (15 minutes)

1. Obtain enough clay so that each student in a group has a ball that is about 5 cm in diameter. Vary the colors of clay in a group so that students can easily observe the different layers in the model stromatolites.

2. Rocks should be about as large as a large grapefruit.

Procedure Tips

1. If necessary, explain that the thin sheet of clay represents a colony of the bacteria that form stromatolites.

2. Inform students that the thicknesses of the layers of clay do *not* have to be uniform within a group or across a single layer of clay. Variations in thicknesses more accurately model actual stromatolites.

Answers

1. Students' models should be very similar to actual stromatolites—rounded and layered.

2. The bacteria that formed stromatolites lived in colonies that were deposited in layers and grew upward to form mounded structures. The outermost, topmost layer is newest; the innermost, bottommost layer is oldest.

Eras Of Earth's History

❓ Answering the Big Question

The activities in this lesson will help students answer the Big Question by having them explore different aspects of geologic time, including how Earth history was divided into eras, what major events mark each era, and the ranges of various life forms.

Inquiry Warm-Up

Dividing History

Inquiry Focus

Communicate—reporting information about a famous person using both words and a timeline

Group Size Individuals

Class Time 15 minutes

Procedure Tips

1. You might want to review students' choices before they do the research.

2. This activity can be streamlined by assigning each student a famous person to research or by providing students with a list of people and allowing them to choose someone from the list.

Answers

1. Students' choices of persons will vary. Criteria will depend on the person and his or her profession or achievements, but might include the person's title, the type of music or art produced, the teams for which the person played, the types of books written, or the types of films in which the person played a role.

2. Look for answers that reasonably explain and support student opinions.

3. The divisions of any timeline are based on the data collected. Different criteria will result in different lengths of time for each subdivision and the development of different timelines.

Quick Lab

Graphing the Fossil Record

Unlocking the Key Concept

This activity will help students realize that different groups of organisms appeared on Earth at different times and that many of the life-forms on Earth today first appeared during the Paleozoic Era.

Inquiry Focus

Graph—organizing data to show when certain groups of organisms appeared on (and sometimes disappeared from) Earth

Group Size Individuals

Class Time 20 minutes

Advance Preparation (10 minutes)
Copy the table below, which lists the ranges of some groups of organisms. Distribute copies to each student.

Procedure Tips

1. It might be useful if you graph one of the ranges given in the table on the overhead projector to get students started. Choose a group that appeared somewhere during the middle part of the Paleozoic so that students realize that the line that represents a range does not necessarily touch the x-axis.

2. In order to make the exercise seem less abstract, you might like to show students photographs of each of the organisms listed in the table.

Answers

1. Pine trees, reptiles, ferns, graptolites, fishes, goniatites, ginkgo trees, trilobites, and club mosses all appeared on Earth during the Paleozoic Era.

2. Graptolites, goniatites, and trilobites became extinct during the Paleozoic Era.

Ranges of Some Major Groups of Organisms on Earth—Graphing the Fossil Record

Organism	Range	Organism	Range
Pine trees	Late Carboniferous to present	Fishes	Late Cambrian to present
Reptiles	Carboniferous to present	Mammals	Late Triassic to present
Dinosaurs	Middle Triassic to Late Cretaceous	Goniatites	Middle Devonian to Late Permian
Ferns	Late Devonian to present	Ginkgo trees	Late Permian to present
Graptolites	Cambrian to Carboniferous	Trilobites	Early Cambrian to Late Permian
Birds	Late Jurassic to present	Club mosses	Early Devonian to present

Quick Lab

Modeling an Asteroid Impact

🔑 Unlocking the Key Concept

This activity will help students visualize how the asteroid impact at the close of the Mesozoic Era might have affected organisms that lived in Earth's shallow seas.

Inquiry Focus

Make Models—creating a physical representation of what could have happened when an asteroid collided with Earth at the close of the Mesozoic Era

Group Size Pairs

Class time 15 minutes

Safety

Remind students to be careful when moving around the darkened room.

Advance Preparation (15 minutes)

1. Premeasure the flour—30 g is about 1 level tablespoon—and place it in a plastic resealable bag.
2. High-intensity flashlights work best for this activity. Make sure the batteries in each flashlight are fresh.
3. Decide how you will darken the room and bring any shades, blankets, or other window coverings to class the day of the activity.

Alternative Materials

Large glass beakers (500 mL) can be used in place of the cups. Students can observe the light—or lack of it—against any opaque surface including a wall, an upright book, or a chalkboard.

Procedure Tips

In Steps 2 and 4, the flashlight should be held so that it is perpendicular to the sides of the cup. It should also be held at the same distance—approximately 1 cm—from the cup in both steps.

Answers

1. The flour represents the dust that was produced when the asteroid collided with Earth. The water represents Earth's oceans.

2. In Step 2, the light passed though the model ocean and could be seen on the cardboard. In Step 4, the flour prevented much of the light from passing through the water.
3. Sample Answer: The dust that formed when the asteroid collided with Earth filled the air. Over time, this dust fell into the oceans and prevented sunlight from penetrating the water. The lack of sunlight caused many organisms in the seas to become extinct.

Quick Lab

Cenozoic Timeline

🔑 Unlocking the Key Concept

This activity will help students learn more about some of the major groups of organisms and events that mark the Cenozoic Era of geologic time.

Inquiry Focus

Communicate—reporting information about the Cenozoic Era

Group Size Individuals

Class Time 20 minutes

Advance Preparation (10 minutes)

Copy the table of major events in the Cenozoic Era on the next page and distribute it to students.

Procedure Tips

If necessary, demonstrate how to construct the timeline so that it is to scale.

Answers

1. The Eocene is the longest epoch; the Holocene is the shortest.
2. Elephants first appeared on Earth during the Pliocene epoch.
3. The Rocky Mountains are older.
4. Look for answers that describe an event that took place during the Cenozoic Era; the event should be one that is listed in the table. If time allows, have students share their findings with the rest of the class.

Major Events in the Cenozoic Era—Cenozoic Timeline

Geologic or Biologic Event	Approximate Date (mya)
Mediterranean Sea dries up.	5
Grasses become widespread.	33.9
Saber-toothed cats appear on Earth.	2.5
Himalaya Mountains begin to form.	50
Antarctica separates from Australia.	37
Glaciers cover much of North America.	1.6
Modern Rocky Mountains start to form.	70
Large asteroid hits eastern North America.	35
Upright walking hominids appear on Earth.	4
Most mammals on Earth weigh less than 10 kg.	55
Ancestors of modern elephants appear on Earth.	5

• 10 min

What's in a Rock?

You've probably seen many rocks from a distance. But have you ever examined a rock up close? In this activity, you will use a hand lens to observe a rock and infer where the parts of the rock came from.

INQUIRY FOCUS Infer

Procedure

Materials

hand lens
rock
colored pencils

1. Use the hand lens to carefully observe the rock sample provided by your teacher. Note the color and texture of the rock and whether or not it contains any unusual imprints or pieces.

2. In the space below, use the colored pencils to make a detailed drawing of the rock.

3. In the space provided, write at least three complete sentences that describe the rock.

_____

_____

_____

Think It Over

1 What do you think the unusual shapes and imprints in your rock are?

_____

_____

2 Infer how the shapes and imprints became parts of the rock.

_____

_____

Name _____ Date _____ Class _____

15 min

Sweet Fossils

Fossils are the preserved remains or traces of once-living things. Most fossils form when living things die and are quickly buried by sediment. In this activity, you will make observations about how fossils of soft parts of organisms form.

INQUIRY FOCUS Observe

Procedure

1. Wrap a piece of the modeling clay around one sugar cube so that half of it is covered with the clay.

2. Wrap another piece of clay entirely around a second sugar cube. Be sure to seal the edges of the clay tightly.

3. Drop both cubes into a bowl of water, along with the third, uncovered sugar cube.

4. Stir the water with the spoon until the uncovered sugar cube dissolves completely.

5. Use the spoon to take the two remaining sugar cubes out of the water. Place them on a paper towel and gently blot them dry. Carefully remove the clay and examine the sugar.

Materials

modeling clay
3 sugar cubes
bowl
warm water
plastic spoon
paper towels

Think It Over

1. Describe the appearance of the two sugar cubes.

_____

_____

2. What effect did the clay have on the sugar?

_____

_____

3. How does this activity model how fossils of soft parts of organisms form?

_____

_____

_____

Quick Lab 15 min

Modeling Trace Fossils

Trace fossils provide evidence of the behavior or activities of ancient organisms. In this activity, you will infer what the trace fossils tell you about the "organism" that made them.

INQUIRY FOCUS Infer

Procedure

Materials

modeling clay
paper plate or waxed paper
small common objects
metric ruler

1. Flatten the clay on the paper plate or waxed paper until the clay is about 10 cm in diameter and 1–2 cm thick.

2. Use one of the objects provided by your teacher to make one type of trace fossil that represents the activity or behavior of an ancient organism. Such fossils might include footprints, trails, or burrows.

3. Exchange your model with the other groups. For each model, describe what you observe and write an inference about the "organism" or its behavior based on your observation.

Describe trace fossil observation	Describe your inference

Think It Over

1 What type of trace fossils did you observe?

_____

_____

2 What were you able to infer about the organisms from the trace fossils left by them?

_____

_____

Name _____ Date _____ Class _____

  25 min

Modeling the Fossil Record

The fossil record provides clues about ancient life forms, how they have changed over time, and what types of environments they lived in. In this activity, you will infer what fossils can tell you about Earth's past.

INQUIRY FOCUS Infer

Procedure

1. Use reference books or the Internet to find out what a geologic cross section looks like. On a piece of paper, use the ruler and colored pencils to draw a geologic cross section with at least four different layers of rocks. Make your layers at least 4 cm thick.

2. Choose one of the following organisms and research how it has changed over time: horse, elephant, shark, or horseshoe crab. Your research should include pictures of the organism during at least four different times in Earth's past. Print the pictures or draw them on paper using colored pencils.

3. ✂ Cut out the pictures and glue or tape them into place on your geologic cross section. Make sure the oldest "fossil" is in the bottom layer of rock and the youngest "fossil" is in the top layer of rock.

Materials

reference books/
  Internet access
blank sheet of paper
colored pencils
metric ruler
scissors
glue or tape

Think It Over

1 Describe how your organism has evolved over time.

_____

_____

2 Why did you put the youngest "fossil" in the top layer of the geologic section?

_____

_____

3 What can you infer about the environment in which your organism lived?

_____

_____

——————————————— **Inquiry Warm-Up** ——————————● **15 min**

Which Layer Is the Oldest?

In rock layers that have not been disturbed, rocks at the bottom of the sequence are the oldest and rocks at the top are the youngest. In this activity, you will observe what happens when rock layers are disturbed.

INQUIRY FOCUS Observe

Procedure

1. Make a model sequence of different-colored layers of clay. Each layer should be about the size and thickness of a pancake. Use this sequence of rocks to answer Question 1.

2. ✂ Now form the stack into a dome by pressing it over a small, rounded object, such as a small bowl. Use the plastic knife to carefully cut off the top of the dome, taking care to leave the bottom layer of clay on the bowl. Look at the layers of rock that are now exposed. Use this model to answer Question 2.

Materials

4 or 5 different colors of modeling clay
small bowl
plastic knife

Think It Over

1 Which layer in your rock sequence is the oldest?

_____

_____

2 Where is the oldest rock layer in the dome?

_____

_____

3 If you had taken the rock sequence in Step 1 and pressed it into the bowl and trimmed away the edges, where would you find the oldest rock layer?

_____

_____

_____

THE RELATIVE AGE OF ROCKS

── • **Lab Investigation**

PRE LAB

Exploring Geologic Time Through Core Samples

Reviewing Content

One way in which scientists study past geologic events is by examining rock layers that are buried beneath Earth's surface. Some of these subsurface rocks formed as magma cooled and hardened deep beneath the crust. Other rocks formed as sediment and the remains of organisms were deposited layer upon layer. The sediment eventually lithified, or turned into rock. Scientists collect samples of such rock layers by driving hollow tubes into the rock and then pulling the tubes out with the rock and fossils inside. This process is called coring. Scientists examine and interpret the core samples to learn more about Earth's long history.

do the math!

The deepest hole ever drilled is about 12,262 km deep and took about 24 years to complete. What is the average number of kilometers drilled per year? About how long would it take you to drive that distance if you were going 75 km/hr?

Reviewing Inquiry Focus

It is said that Earth's present is the key to its past. This means that many Earth scientists make observations about organisms and processes on Earth today and use these observations to interpret rocks and fossils that formed long ago.

1 In this investigation, what observations will you be making?

_____

_____

2 What type of dating method will you be using in this investigation?

_____

_____

DIRECTED Inquiry ● 40 min

Exploring Geologic Time Through Core Samples

Problem

What do rocks and fossils tell you about Earth's past?

INQUIRY FOCUS
Observe, Make Models, Measure

Materials

1-L milk carton, clean and empty, with its top cut off

sediment loose clay or red-colored sand, white-colored sand, potting soil or mud

"fossils" rice, barley, millet, lentils, split peas

water in spray bottle

small scoops or plastic cups

mixing bowl

plastic spoon

thick, hard plastic drinking straws

wooden or plastic rod that fits into the straws

several sheets of paper

metric ruler

hand lens

Procedure

1. 🛡️ 🦺 Put on your safety goggles and apron.

2. Decide on the type and order of sediment that will be placed in your milk carton. Plan to use all three types of sediment and at least three types of fossils. You will have more than one layer of each type of sediment.

3. In the milk carton outline on the left in Step 11 on the next page, draw the order of the sediment layers and their approximate thicknesses. Record also the type and placement of fossils in the layers.

4. 🖐️ Assemble your model, using the diagram you just made as a guide. For the bottom layer, put two or three scoopfuls of the bottommost sediment in the bowl. Use the spoon to mix in a few spoonfuls of "fossils." Carefully pour the mixture in the bottom of the milk carton. Use the spray bottle to add a small amount of water so the sediment becomes slightly damp. Sweep or wipe up any spills immediately.

5. Continue this process, following your sediment order, until the carton is almost full. You can make the sediment layers different thicknesses, but keep them horizontal.

6. Without tilting the milk carton, exchange your model with one prepared by another group.

7. Now collect a core sample from this container. Hold a straw vertically near the surface of the sediment and slowly push it straight down into the sediment. Push until your straw is close to the bottom of the milk carton.

8. Fold a sheet of paper in half lengthwise. Write *Top* at the top and *Bottom* at the bottom of the paper. You will use the crease in the paper to hold the core sample after you remove the sample from the straw.

DIRECTED Inquiry   • **Lab Investigation**

**EXPLORING GEOLOGIC TIME
THROUGH CORE SAMPLES** *continued*

9. Gently pull the straw out of the sediment container and lay it in the crease of the paper with the top of the straw at the top of the paper. Using the rod, carefully push the sediment out of the bottom of the straw into the crease of the folded paper so that the core sample rests in the crease. Slowly pull the straw back as you push the sample out. The top of the sample should be near the top of the paper.

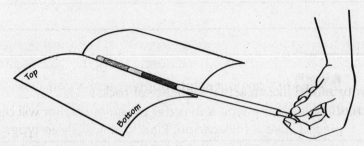

10. In the milk container diagram on the right, draw the sediment layers in the correct order as they appear in your core sample. Measure the thickness of each layer in the core sample in centimeters, and write the measurements next to the recorded layers.

11. Look through the sediment layers, one at a time, for "fossils." Use a hand lens to help you. Because the fossils are small, you might need to take several core samples to find any fossils. Draw the fossils you find in the correct sediment layer.

12. Wash your hands with warm water and soap.

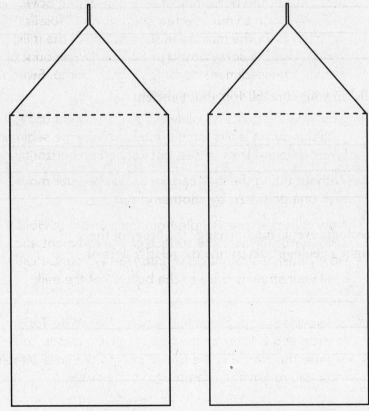

Your group's layers   **Layers from the other group**

THE RELATIVE AGE OF ROCKS

**EXPLORING GEOLOGIC TIME
THROUGH CORE SAMPLES** *continued*

Analyze and Conclude

1 **Observe** In the core you examined, which "rock" layer is the oldest? Which is the youngest? How do you know?

_____

_____

_____

2 **Make Models** How is your model like an actual sequence of rocks? How is your model different?

_____

_____

_____

_____

3 **Interpret Data** Are there any index fossils in your core? Explain.

_____

_____

_____

_____

4 **Infer** What do the "fossils" in your core tell you about ancient life forms?

_____

_____

_____

5 **Predict** What types of geologic events might change the order of the rocks in an area? How might a geologist determine the relative ages of the disturbed rocks?

_____

_____

_____

_____

THE RELATIVE AGE OF ROCKS

POST LAB

Exploring Geologic Time
Through Core Samples

1 **Infer** Why did you take your core vertically without tilting the straw?

_____

_____

_____

_____

2 **Draw Conclusions** What did you learn about the model rocks from
your core?

_____

_____

_____

_____

3 **Summarize** Describe what you learned in this lab about coring a
section of "rock" and what questions you still have.

What I learned _____

_____

_____

_____

What I still want to know _____

_____

_____

_____

Communicate

Compare the drawing of the core you made with the drawing made by the group
that made the core. Note the similarities and differences.

THE RELATIVE AGE OF ROCKS

OPEN Inquiry ————————● **40 min**

Exploring Geologic Time Through Core Samples
Problem

What do rocks and fossils tell you about Earth's past?

INQUIRY FOCUS
Make Models,
Observe

Materials

half gallon milk
 carton, emptied
 and rinsed

four different fine
 sediments, such
 as red sand, white
 sand, potting
 soil, dried coffee
 grounds

flour

fossils: a variety of
 small seeds and
 grains such as rice,
 lentils, sesame
 seeds

mixing bowl

large diameter
 drinking straw

long dowel or rod
 that fits into the
 straw

several sheets of
 paper

metric ruler

gloves

Design an Experiment

1. Your group will produce a set of rock layers, with fossils included, for another group to analyze.

2. Determine how you will layer the sediments provided by your teacher, in terms of oldest and youngest, as well as the thickness of each layer.

3. Assign certain "fossils" to the specific layers, and choose one fossil to be an index fossil.

4. Once you and your partner have a plan or "blueprint" for your rock layer model, sketch that plan in the space provided below.

**THE RELATIVE AGE OF ROCKS**

OPEN Inquiry — **Lab Investigation**

EXPLORING GEOLOGIC TIME
THROUGH CORE SAMPLES *continued*

5. ✋ ⚠ After your teacher has had a look at your blueprint, build your model by mixing the bottom-most sediment layer and its characteristic fossils in the mixing bowl, pouring it into the container, and adding a bit of water to make the layer a bit denser and packed down. Repeat with each of the other layers until your layers have been laid down according to your blueprint. One fossil should be an index fossil that is placed in just one layer of sediment.

6. Swap your model with that of another group, according to your teacher's instructions. Now you will analyze the characteristics and fossils of the other group's model by taking three core samples. The straw is the corer, the rod is for gently pushing the core sample out onto a piece of paper, and the ruler is for measuring the thickness of each layer of sediment. Before you put these tools to work, consider the following questions:

- How might you set up the paper to keep each core sample in place so you can carefully analyze it?

- How should you mark the paper so that you maintain the law of superposition as you study the core sample?

- How can you quantify the thickness of each layer and the types of fossils they contain?

7. Use the space provided below to record your findings and sketch the composition of the model in the same way that you sketched the one that your group built.

8. Wash your hands with warm water and soap when you are finished.

Data Table

THE RELATIVE AGE OF ROCKS

Name _____ Date _____ Class _____

Analyze and Conclude

1 **Observe** How many rock layers were there? Describe the rock layers.
What was the order of layers from oldest to youngest, and which fossil
was the index fossil?

_____
_____
_____
_____

2 **Infer** How did you identify the index fossil?

_____
_____
_____
_____

3 **Make Models** Take the model back to the group that built it.
Compare your findings with their blueprint for the model. Describe
how your findings compare with the blueprint.

_____
_____
_____
_____

4 **Design an Experiment** What could you have done during the core
sampling phase of this activity to get more data and perhaps come closer
to getting the results that the model's builders expected you to get?

_____
_____
_____
_____

THE RELATIVE AGE OF ROCKS

POST LAB

Exploring Geologic Time Through Core Samples

1 **Design an Experiment** List some ideas for improving both the model construction and the core sampling parts of this activity.

_____

_____

_____

2 **Infer** In the real world, how would core sampling differ from what you modeled in this activity? Explain.

_____

_____

_____

3 **Form a Hypothesis** How could core sampling be useful in determining a safe site for the construction of a skyscraper? Explain.

_____

_____

_____

4 **Draw Conclusions** How is looking at the walls of the Grand Canyon like taking a core sample?

_____

_____

_____

Communicate

You are a paleontologist being interviewed for a newscast. An unknown species has shown up in the form of a fossil dug up from a nearby quarry. Describe how you might use core sampling at the same site and at other sites to determine the relative age of this unknown species. Make a video of your interview, and be sure to discuss the following:

• the law of superposition
• index fossils
• the process of taking and examining core samples

THE RELATIVE AGE OF ROCKS

Name _____ Date _____ Class _____

How Did It Form?

When rocks are folded, faulted, or eroded, geologists must closely examine them to determine their relative ages. In this activity, you will make two model rock sequences and observe what happens when the rocks are deformed.

INQUIRY FOCUS Make Models

Procedure

Materials

- 6 different colors of modeling clay
- metric ruler
- plastic knife

1. Refer to the diagram of unconformities and folding in your textbook. Use the clay to make a model of the rock sequence shown in the diagram. Your model should be about 15 cm wide. Each of the rock layers should be between 1 and 2 cm thick, and all of the layers must be horizontal.

2. ✂ Use the plastic knife to carefully cut your model in half vertically so that you have two equal rock-sequence halves with horizontal layers.

3. Use the drawings on the left side of the diagram to deform one of your rock sequence halves.

4. Deform the other half of your rock sequence using the drawings on the right side of the diagram.

Think It Over

1 Explain how the rock layers changed when they were deformed using the path on the left side of the diagram. Identify, by color, the oldest and youngest rock layers.

_____

_____

_____

2 Explain how the rock layers changed when they were deformed using the path on the right side of the diagram. Identify, by color, the oldest and youngest rock layers.

_____

_____

_____

THE RELATIVE AGE OF ROCKS

Inquiry Warm-Up   10 min

How Long Till It's Gone?

Some elements on Earth are unstable and break down, or decay, over time. In this activity, you will model this type of decay and predict how much of the element will remain after a certain amount of time.

INQUIRY FOCUS Predict

Procedure

1. Make a small cube—about 5 cm × 5 cm × 5 cm— from the modeling clay.

2. ✂ Carefully use the plastic knife to cut the cube in half. Put one half of the clay cube aside.

3. Make a prediction about how much of the original cube will remain after you have cut it in half two more times.

_____

4. Cut the clay cube in front of you in half two more times. Each time you cut the cube, put one half of it aside.

Materials

modeling clay
metric ruler
plastic knife

Think It Over

1 How big is the clay cube you have been cutting compared to the original size of the cube?

_____

_____

2 How big will the remaining piece of the cube be if you were to cut it in half three more times?

_____

_____

3 Suppose you started with a clay cube that was 10 cm on each side. If you cut it in half three times, how big would the piece be compared to the original cube?

_____

_____

RADIOACTIVE DATING

Name _____ Date_____ Class_____

The Dating Game

The time it takes for half the number of radioactive atoms to decay is the half-life of the element. In this activity, you will use pennies and a stopwatch or clock to model half-life.

INQUIRY FOCUS Graph

Procedure

1. Place all of the pennies in the cup. Check the time on the stopwatch and record it below.

Start Time _____   End Time _____

2. Dump the pennies into the pan. Take out all of the pennies that landed heads up and count them. Pennies that land heads up represent atoms of an element that have decayed. Create a data table in your notebook to record your results.

3. Take the remaining pennies—those that landed tails up—and put them back into the cup. These pennies represent atoms that have not decayed. Dump them into the pan. Take out all of the pennies that landed heads up and count them. Record your results in the data table.

4. Repeat Step 3 two more times. Remember to record your results. After the last trial, check and record the time shown on the stopwatch or clock. Record this End Time in Step 1 above.

5. Create a bar graph of your results in your notebook. Give your graph a title.

Materials

100 pennies
plastic cup
aluminum pan
stopwatch or clock

Think It Over

1 How does this activity model half-life? What does each set of coins represent?

_____

_____

2 Use your start and end times to calculate the half-life of your "radioactive" element.

_____

_____

_____ **Quick Lab** _____● 10 min

How Old Is It?

Scientists can calculate how many half-lives have passed by first determining how much radioactive element is left in a rock. Then they compare that with the amount of stable element into which the radioactive element decayed.

INQUIRY FOCUS Calculate

Procedure

1. Read the lab report summary about your rock or fossil carefully.

2. To determine the approximate age of your rock or fossil, you must multiply the number of half-lives that have passed by the half-life of the element.

   approximate age = number of half-lives that have passed × half-life (years)

3. Use a calculator, the equation above, and the table below to determine the age of your rock or fossil. Make a data table in which to record the object and its age.

4. Repeat Step 3 with three more lab report summaries. Record your answers in your data table.

Materials

calculator
lab report summary

Elements Used in Radioactive Dating

Radioactive Element	Half-life (years)	Dating Range
Carbon-14	5,730	500-50,000
Potassium-40	1.3 billion	50,000–4.6 billion
Rubidium-87	48.8 billion	10 million–4.6 billion
Thorium-232	14 billion	10 million–4.6 billion
Uranium-235	713 million	10 million–4.6 billion
Uranium-238	4.5 billion	10 million–4.6 billion

Think It Over

1 Which fossil or rock is the oldest? Which is the youngest?

_____

2 Which rocks or fossils were dated using carbon-14? Why?

_____

Inquiry Warm-Up · 15 min

This Is Your Life!

Many events have taken place in your life. In this activity, you will list some of the more important events and make a timeline to show when these events occurred.

INQUIRY FOCUS Make Models

Procedure

1. In the space below, make a list of 10 to 15 important events that you recall in your life. List the events in any order.

_____

_____

_____

_____

_____

Materials

metric ruler
graph paper

2. Turn the graph paper so that the long edge is parallel to the edge of your desk. Use the ruler to draw a timeline to represent your life. Use a scale of 2.0 cm to 1 year. Label the years on your time line from your birth year to the present year.

3. Write each event from Step 1 in the correct year along the timeline.

4. Now divide the timeline into parts that describe major periods in your life, such as preschool years, elementary school years, and middle school years.

Think It Over

1 Along which part of your timeline are most of the events located?

_____

_____

2 How can you explain your answer to Question 1?

_____

_____

THE GEOLOGIC TIME SCALE

_____ **Quick Lab** ●————— 25 min

Going Back in Time

Because geologic time is so long, it is useful to relate this time to something
with which you are familiar. In this activity, you and your classmates will mark
the eras and periods of the geologic time scale in a long stretch of space.

INQUIRY FOCUS Make Models

Procedure

Materials

one sheet of white poster
  board per student

black, blue, green, and
  orange markers

meter stick

long hallway

1. Your teacher will assign one person to represent
   Precambrian time. This person will write *Precambrian
   Time* in large, black capital letters on a piece of
   poster board. All of the other students will represent
   a geologic era or a geologic period.

2. Refer to the Geologic Time Scale in your student
   edition. Use the colors in the figure to write the name
   of your era or period on your piece of poster board.
   For example, if you were assigned the Paleozoic era,
   you would write the name of the era in large, capital letters using a blue marker. If
   you were assigned a period within the Paleozoic era, you would write the name of
   the period in large, blue letters. Note that geologic periods should have only the
   first letter of their names capitalized.

3. Take your poster board and, with your teacher, go to the designated area.

4. Your teacher will tell you where to place your poster board along the hallway.

5. Walk along the hallway, starting with the Precambrian, to answer the questions.

Think It Over

1 How many meters does Precambrian time span?

_____

2 Why is Precambrian time so much longer than the rest of Earth history
     put together?

_____

3 Based on what you can see on the model, what can you say about how long the
     Paleozoic era lasted compared to the Mesozoic era?

_____

Inquiry Warm-Up · 10 min

How Could Planet Earth Form in Space?

Scientists think that Earth formed about 4.6 billion years ago as gravity pulled dust, rock, and ice particles in space into a sphere. In this activity, you will model how our planet may have formed.

INQUIRY FOCUS Make Models

Procedure

1. 🥽 Put on your safety goggles and wear them for the entire activity.

2. Place the sheet of paper on top of the magnet. The paper represents outer space and the magnet models gravity.

3. Sprinkle a half teaspoon of iron filings along one end of the paper to model the materials that formed Earth.

4. Gently blow through a straw for about 10 seconds from the end of the paper with the iron filings toward the magnet. **CAUTION:** *Be sure the straw is pointed away from other students.*

5. Observe what happens to the iron filings. Draw what you observe in the box below.

6. 🧼 Return the iron filings to your teacher and wash your hands well.

Materials

- circular magnet
- iron filings
- teaspoon
- sheet of plain white paper
- straw

Think It Over

1 What would happen to the size of "Earth" if you repeated Steps 3 and 4?

_____

_____

2 How is this activity similar to how Earth might have formed? How is the activity different?

_____

_____

_____

Quick Lab

20 min

Learning From Fossils

Many stromatolites are found in Precambrian rocks. Stromatolites form when certain minerals in seawater stick to bacteria growing nearby. In this activity, you will model the formation of stromatolites.

INQUIRY FOCUS Infer

Procedure

1. Take turns with the other students in your group to place your portion of clay between two pieces of waxed paper and use the rolling pin to flatten the clay into a thin (0.5–1.0-cm) sheet.

2. Remove the top sheet of wax paper. Drape the flattened clay over the rock. Gently peel back the other sheet of waxed paper.

3. Have each student in your group repeat Step 2 with his or her flattened clay.

4. Use the plastic knife to cut through the clay layers to make a cross-section of the structure as follows. Start at the bottom of the rock and glide the knife up the rock, over the top, and back down the other side of the clay-covered rock.

5. Carefully remove the layered clay from the rock.

6. In the space below, draw the cross-sectional view of the layers of clay.

Materials

clay
rolling pin
waxed paper
medium-sized rock
plastic knife
metric ruler

Think It Over

1 In what ways are actual stromatolites similar to your model?

_____

_____

2 How did the addition of new layers of clay model the addition of new material to a stromatolite? Which layer is newest and which is oldest?

_____

_____

Dividing History

A person's life can be divided into segments based on achievements or other notable events. In this activity, you will divide a person's life into blocks of time and compare this to how geologic time is divided.

INQUIRY FOCUS Communicate

Procedure

1. Choose a famous person, such as a politician, an artist, an athlete, a musician, an author, or a movie star.

2. Use the reference books or Internet to find out about the person's life. Choose what information you will record, such as his or her career, family life, personal achievements, and so on. Be sure to note dates and names as you record your data.

3. Divide the person's life into three separate segments based on criteria that you chose.

4. On the sheet of paper, use the metric ruler to make a timeline of the person's life. Include events or accomplishments achieved during each of the three sections of time. Your timeline must include dates and names for the three sections of time.

5. Exchange timelines with another student. Discuss the timelines and how they were constructed.

Materials

- reference books/ Internet access
- sheet of plain white paper
- metric ruler

Think It Over

1. Who did you choose and what types of criteria did you use to divide his or her life into blocks of time?

_____
_____

2. Do you agree or disagree with how the timeline you got from another student is divided? Explain.

_____
_____

3. Why is it important to establish the criteria on which a time scale will be based?

_____
_____

Quick Lab

Graphing the Fossil Record

Many of the billions of different organisms that have lived on Earth first appeared during the Paleozoic Era. In this activity, you will graph the ranges of various life forms.

INQUIRY FOCUS Graph

Procedure

Materials

graph paper
metric ruler
colored pencils
table with ranges of
   groups of organisms

1. Refer to the information about the Geologic Time Scale in your textbook. On the graph paper, label each geologic period along the y-axis. Place the Cambrian at the bottom of the axis and the Quaternary at the top of the axis. Leave only one block between each period. Label the x-axis to read "Ranges of Some Major Organisms on Earth."

2. On your graph, use the metric ruler to plot the range of each group of organisms listed in the table provided by your teacher. Use a different-colored pencil for each group of organisms. Label each line with the name of the organism.

Note: The range of a group of organisms is the length of time the organisms have lived on Earth. Ranges are often shown by vertical lines on a graph. The bottom of the line marks the time the organisms first appeared. The top of the line indicates that the organisms are still alive or marks the point when they became extinct.

Think It Over

1 Which groups of organisms first appeared during the Paleozoic Era?

_____

2 Which groups of organisms became extinct during the Paleozoic Era?

_____

Quick Lab

15 min

Modeling an Asteroid Impact

You know that dinosaurs and other organisms that lived on land became extinct when an asteroid hit Earth at the close of the Cretaceous Period. But did you know that this impact also affected organisms in the seas?

INQUIRY FOCUS Make Models

Procedure

1. Pour cold water into the cup until the cup is about three-fourths full. Place the cup on a desk or table.

2. Darken the room. Have your partner hold the cardboard 15 cm behind the cup as you shine the flashlight through the water. Observe the cardboard.

3. Turn off the flashlight. Add the flour to the water a little at a time. Stir the mixture with the spoon as you add the flour.

4. Once you have added all of the flour to the water, have your partner hold the cardboard 15 cm behind the cup as you shine the flashlight through the water. Observe the cardboard.

Materials

plastic cup
flashlight
cold water
30 g white baking flour
plastic spoon
metric ruler
sheet of white cardboard

Think It Over

1 What do the flour and water used in this activity represent?

_____

_____

2 How did your observations differ in Steps 2 and 4?

_____

_____

3 Use your observations to explain how an asteroid impact could have affected organisms that lived in the oceans at the close of the Mesozoic Era.

_____

_____

Name _____ Date_____ Class_____

Cenozoic Timeline

Geologic periods are subdivided into units called epochs. In this activity, you will make a timeline of some of the major events that took place during each of the seven epochs of the Cenozoic Era.

INQUIRY FOCUS Communicate

Procedure

1. ✂ Cut the graph paper in half lengthwise and tape the pieces together to form a long horizontal strip.

2. Use the ruler and information below to draw a timeline that is divided into seven sections—one section for each epoch. Use the graph paper's grid to make the timeline to scale. Make the Holocene epoch the 0 point on your timeline.
   Note: The geologic periods of the Cenozoic Era are broken down into seven epochs. The Paleocene epoch began about 65 million years ago (mya). The Eocene began about 55 mya. The Oligocene began about 34 mya. The Miocene started about 24 mya. The Pliocene began about 5 mya. The Pleistocene began about 2 mya. The Holocene began about 0.01 mya.

3. Plot each event listed in the table provided by your teacher in the correct place on your timeline.

Materials

- sheet of graph paper
- scissors
- tape
- metric ruler
- table of major events in the Cenozoic era

Think It Over

1 Which epoch of the Cenozoic Era was the longest? The shortest?

_____

2 During which epoch did ancestors of modern elephants appear on Earth?

_____

3 Which are older—the Rocky Mountains or the Himalaya Mountains?

_____

4 Research one of the events listed in the table to learn more about it. Record your findings on another sheet of paper.

ERAS OF EARTH'S HISTORY

Common SI Units

Measurement	Unit	Symbol	Equivalents
Length	1 millimeter 1 centimeter 1 meter 1 kilometer	mm cm m km	1,000 micrometers (µm) 10 millimeters (mm) 100 centimeters (cm) 1,000 meters (m)
Area	1 square meter 1 square kilometer	m^2 km^2	10,000 square centimeters (cm^2) 1,000,000 square meters (m^2)
Volume	1 milliliter 1 liter	mL L	1 cubic centimeter (cm^3 or cc) 1,000 milliliters (mL)
Mass	1 gram 1 kilogram 1 ton	g kg t	1,000 milligrams (mg) 1,000 grams (g) 1,000 kilograms (kg) = 1 ton
Time	1 second	s	
Temperature	1 Kelvin	K	1 degree Celsius (°C)

Metric Conversion Tables

When You Know	Multiply by	To Find	When You Know	Multiply by	To Find
inches	2.54	centimeters	centimeters	0.394	inches
feet	0.3048	meters	meters	3.281	feet
yards	0.914	meters	meters	1.0936	yards
miles	1.609	kilometers	kilometers	0.62	miles
square inches	6.45	square centimeters	square centimeters	0.155	square inches
square feet	0.093	square meters	square meters	10.76	square feet
square yards	0.836	square meters	square meters	1.196	square yards
acres	0.405	hectares	hectares	2.471	acres
square miles	2.59	square kilometers	square kilometers	0.386	square miles
cubic inches	16.387	cubic centimeters	cubic centimeters	0.061	cubic inches
cubic feet	0.028	cubic meters	cubic meters	35.315	cubic feet
cubic yards	0.765	cubic meters	cubic meters	1.31	cubic yards
fluid ounces	29.57	milliliters	milliliters	0.0338	fluid ounces
quarts	0.946	liters	liters	1.057	quarts
gallons	3.785	liters	liters	0.264	gallons
ounces	28.35	grams	grams	0.0353	ounces
pounds	0.4536	kilograms	kilograms	2.2046	pounds
tons	0.907	metric tons	metric tons	1.102	tons

When You Know		
Fahrenheit	subtract 32; then divide by 1.8	to find Celsius
Celsius	multiply by 1.8; then add 32	to find Fahrenheit

GRAPH PAPER

STUDENT SAFETY TEST ANSWERS

p. xxiii

Part 1

Refer to page xix and page xx for the meanings of each of the symbols.

p. xxiv

Part 2

The location of the safety equipment will depend on the classroom.

Analyze and Conclude

1. He is not wearing safety goggles.
2. She is not wearing safety goggles. She does not have an apron on. Her hair should be tied back. She should not add the water to the acid. She should add the acid to the water.
3. He should not be heating something in a closed container.

p. xxv

Critical Thinking and Applications

1. No; she should not drink in the lab.
2. Yes
3. Yes
4. No; always wear shoes in the lab.
5. No; no horseplay is allowed in lab.
6. No; always follow correct lab procedures.

p. xxvii

Laboratory Skills Checkup 2

1. A
2. E
3. B
4. G
5. F
6. C
7. D

p. xxviii

Laboratory Skills Checkup 3

A. 7
B. 5
C. 8
D. 6
E. 1, 2
F. 2, 3, 4

p. xxix

Laboratory Skills Checkup 4

A. 9
B. 5
C. 4, 7, 8
D. 6
E. 1
F. 6, 7
G. Amount of salt added to the water
H. The freezing temperature of the water

p. xxx

Laboratory Skills Checkup 5

1. He did not put on his safety goggles. He should not have broken the rock into two pieces without checking with his teacher first.
2. He should have used the units on the graduated cylinder for volume. Also, he should have used the unit gram for mass. An ounce is a unit of weight.
3. He should have written the data in his notebook.
4. He should have used the balance to find the mass of the rock.
5. In science, always use metric units.
6. He did not divide the mass of the rock by the volume of the rock.

128